Whatever It Takes

By

Doug Wead

Printed in the United States of America

Typesetting by Type-O-Graphics
Springfield, Missouri 65806

Contents

Dedication

Dedicated to my beautiful wife Jacki; for her faithful support through the years of struggle, and for her encouragement to do "Whatever it Takes" to come out victorious.

Chapter 1

Strangers in the Night

A haze of smoke from cigarettes and marijuana enveloped the air as partially-filled, lip-smudged glasses reeked nauseating odors throughout the dressing room. Loud conversations ceased momentarily for a swig of liquor or a "toke" on a joint, while sleazily clad girls nestled closely to their boyfriends on the shiny, black vinyl couch.

"Quick Bobby, let me have a few hits before we go back on."

His second toke was interrupted by the short, but lively nightclub host's introduction, "Let's hear it for Sammy Hall and the Birdwatchers!" The seductive pull of the drug had a hold on one arm, whispering to him to skip the set; but he couldn't escape the opposite pull of reality and his need for the money which supported him and the band.

"C'mon Sammy, we've gotta get out there! They're waiting on us!"

After a few moments, Bobby ripped the joint

from Sammy's mouth and nudged him out the door, past the broken tables and outdated sound equipment sitting in the hallway. He made his usual trot to the stage, his sequined shirt and silk pants hugging tightly to his skin, his hair bouncing from his shoulders. The applause made him forget the joint and he began checking out the girls in the audience for "winners." He'd scored his first night here and every night since. In fact, the group had a running competition to see who could score the most each night. Five or six times was considered good, performing 30 minutes on stage and then 30 minutes in a car throughout the evening.

The nightclub, "Trader John's", later changed to "The Climax", was one of the swingingest spots in the Miami, Florida area. Actually it was located on a four-lane highway in Hialeah, a suburb of Miami, on which students from nearby Dade Junior College would race their high-powered engines or park them for display at a hamburger stand across from the club.

By its appearance it looked innocent enough, the dull gray building with no windows, surrounded by Australian pines and palm trees, with a large red blinking neon sign and a marquee that read, "Now Appearing: Florida's #1 Group, Sammy Hall and the Birdwatchers." Allegedly however, it was a headquarters for drugs in Miami, the audiences a far cry from the congregations Sammy had sung to as a boy in church. Pushers descended upon the place in hoards, and one could get any type of high he wanted. Lots of money floated around from the rich "birds" who migrated south to take advantage of the warm climate. It wasn't uncommon to hear that someone had been shot or disappeared in the immediate vicinity, and rumors had it that the mafia was in the area as well.

It was 1966, and the Birdwatchers were seemingly on their way to national stardom, spending half their time at the club and the other half on the road giving rock concerts to thousands of teenagers on the East Coast. They had appeared with the Beach Boys, Glenn Campbell, the Young Rascals, Paul Revere and the Raiders, and Roy Orbison. They also performed on Dick Clark's TV show "Where the Action Is," a sixties version of "Americn Bandstand." Their popularity had skyrocketed when they appeared in a movie called "The Wild Rebels," and Billboard Magazine pointed to them as the "new group to watch."

Upon reaching the stage he was momentarily blinded by the flashing lights, but midway through his first number his eyes started to adjust and he put his "roving eye" into action. Tables on both sides of the waxed dance floor were full, and crowded at the large circular bar near the back were all the guys with their drinks in one hand looking over the available herd.

At first it looked like a loser's night. There were the usual groups of college girls here for the first time looking for a new source of excitement, and the couples closely embraced behind candlelight, occasionally emerging from the privacy of their darkened corner to dance in the open light, in love with each other, and oblivious to those crowded around them. Then Sammy spotted a few older guys who fit the executive mold, here to escape the pressures of work and home, but feeling out of place with their short hair and obvious age difference.

Suddenly, beneath a red and white checkered tablecloth he spotted a nice pair of legs. Up from there things looked even better until he noticed her boyfriend. Nevertheless, she was a gorgeous blonde who couldn't have been over 18 and had to be in on a fake ID. Sammy almost forgot his lyrics he was so intrigued by this new face. He was tired of the girls he could have at the snap of his fingers. He even thought to himself, "that looks like the type of girl I'd like to marry," but keeping it to himself for fear of what the guys in the group would think if they knew he would ever stoop to marriage. "She's got real class. I've got to meet her, boyfriend or no boyfriend."

While singing *Groovy Kind of Love* he saw her and her date get up to dance. Sammy's eyes never left her, which became easier as she danced right toward the stage. The closer she got the more he desired to meet her. Before long she was right below him. After the song was over, to Sammy's amazement, she asked him "Why don't you ever smile?"

Without hesitation he snapped, "I don't have anything to smile about." The blonde hastily retreated, leaving Sammy thinking he had made a fool out of himself.

Realizing he'd just blown the opportunity he'd hoped for, he went to the bouncer for help. Only if one was desperate enough would they even come near him. Someone said "Spike" served time in the state penitentiary for assault and battery. It was believable. His forearms were bigger than most men's thighs. He had doubled as a waiter until they discovered he was demanding larger tips from the customers. He was a fairly good looking man, but his constant frown didn't make him very pleasant to look at.

"Hey Spike, do me a favor, will ya? See that tall blonde in the blue dress—how 'bout getting her phone number for me?"

"I'll bring her backstage if you'd like."

"Nah, I don't want to hassle with her boyfriend tonight. Just get her number."

"I'll take care of him, just watch," he growled.

"Seriously man," as Sammy grabbed his arm, "just get the number."

It was Monday, his day off, so he called her, but she already had a date for the night. Her name was Jacki Merletti, an airline stewardess. Although their conversation was short, he could tell she was interested because she said he could call her again sometime.

Things were pretty dead that night so he

stopped in at the club. While talking to the bartender, Sammy spotted Jacki with her date. He sat there for a few minutes trying to get up enough courage to go talk to her. "Benny, give me a shot of some hard stuff. I'm gonna need all the guts I can get." Finally deciding on what approach to use, Sammy walked right past her table and in a sudden motion wheeled toward her.

"Jacki! How ya been? It must be five years since I saw you last. You're looking great. Hey, aren't you gonna introduce me to your date?"

Before she had a chance to say a word Sammy broke in, "listen buddy, you wouldn't mind if two old friends had a dance would ya?" Without waiting for a response, Sammy had her half way out of her seat. As they walked away they heard a faint but hesitant voice say "go ahead."

"You've got a lot of nerve," she said harshly. "What gives you the right to break in on our conversation?"

His smiling teeth just gleamed back at her in silence.

"What's wrong with you; are you loaded?"

"No, I just wanted to show you that I can smile just as much as you can."

"Listen Sammy, I'm sorry if I upset you the other night, but really, you should loosen up a little and have a good time while you're performing. I like your sound, but you've got to act like you enjoy what you're doing. Why don't you smile more, aren't you happy?"

His smile faded slowly away. "No, I guess I'm not."

"Well, why not?"

"I don't know. I guess this is just a lonely business," he answered, "and sometimes the club gets to me. You get tired of the same old routine. It doesn't give me the excitement it used to." All the while he thought of his life of drugs and sex, but was afraid to give her any notion of them.

"What would make you happy, Sammy?"

"Only you," he said as a smile returned to his face.

"I'm trying to be serious."

"I am too," he exclaimed.

She gave him an unsure look, "but we don't even know each other."

"That's going to change." Leading her back to her table he told her he'd call her the following day. "Oh, thanks again, friend for allowing us to dance, and Jacki, take care, and I hope I don't have to wait five years to see you again."

The next evening they went to the club together. His performance was different than most that night. He sang as if he was enjoying himself. The music flowed through his body, moving the crowd like never before. They began clapping in unison, dancing on tables, their blood racing through their veins, alcohol down their throats. The crowd was at his fingertips, screaming for "more, more, more!" But inside he screamed only for more of Jacki. She'd given him a reason to be happy. His music for the first time had a purpose. Between shows he slid in beside her and got to know her better.

"Where do your parents live?" Jacki asked.

"Ft. Lauderdale," Sammy answered.

"I'd sure like to meet them someday."

Sammy responded, "That would be nice, I'm sure they'd like that," although thinking to himself how embarrassing it could be if they started preaching to her. "I want you to meet Jeff too," Sammy added.

"Who's Jeff?"

"He's my little nephew; probably my best friend. We do almost everything together: go fishing, to the park, for rides."

"It sounds like you're real close," Jacki said.

"We are," Sammy nodded, thinking that Jeff didn't hassle him about God like the rest of the family.

Sammy's family was very religious; in fact, he got his start singing in a small Pentecostal church in Sanford, North Carolina, where his father would accompany him on the guitar. Church became a bore and although he was forced to go, he made up enough excuses not to sing that he wasn't asked anymore. He always believed in God, just not church. As his involvement in church decreased, his experiences with shoplifting and later alcohol and drugs increased.

After the last show of the evening he drove her home in his shiny chromed, metallic-green

Riviera. When they pulled up to her apartment complex Jacki told him he looked a lot happier tonight.

"You're really hung up on this happiness kick, aren't you? Don't worry about me, this unhappiness thing will pass. Thanks for caring though," he said as he leaned over and kissed her.

"You know girl, I've got a feelin' I'm going to marry you someday. Would you marry me?"

Laughing it off she said, "So you're asking me to marry you on our first date," although wondering just how serious he was.

"Does that mean you won't?" Sammy teasingly pouted.

"So you're serious, huh?" she continued to laugh.

Sammy didn't respond; instead, he led her to the door and kissed her goodnight. As she stepped inside Sammy felt like wedging his foot in the door and telling her he didn't want to leave her. For when that door was completely closed it shut him back inside a world of unhappiness. He stood at her door a few seconds, wanting to break it down and wrap her in his arms, but realistically wondering if he should just knock. Finally he left when his trance was interrupted by a moth's orbit around a light above his head.

At 10:30 the next morning Sammy came to a screeching halt outside the club, nearly missing the large neon sign. He was 30 minutes late for a publicity picture session. Before he walked in, he prepared himself for the ribbing he was going to get from the guys for being late. Sure enough, all four of them had smirks on their faces. There was Bobby Piccitti, manager and organist; Joey Murcia, lead guitarist; Jerry Schills, bass guitarist; and drummer, Eddie Martinez.

"What's the matter, Sammy, was she more than you could handle last night?" Joey teased. The whole band convulsed with laughter.

"What'd you mean by that, man?"

"Well did you score with the 'good looker' you were with last night, or did you strike out?"

"I didn't even try; she means too much to me."

"Either you're just losing your touch or you're turning religious on us."

"Listen, jerk," Sammy snarled as he grabbed Joey's shirt, "I don't have to put up with your garbage."

"Just because you let a good one get away, don't blame us. That's your problem," Joey yelled back.

"Your problem is that you wanted her for yourself," Sammy said, taking a firmer hold on his shirt and sending Joey flying over a chair. Later, after he had stormed out angry enough to tear down the building, he returned.

"Hey guys, I'm sorry, I've just had a lot on my mind lately. And Joey, I didn't hurt ya, did I? I'm sorry man, can we get on with the pictures?"

A few days later he stopped by Jacki's apartment. When he knocked on her door, she was in the process of writing a letter to her boyfriend telling him she had met someone else. They had gone together since her sophomore year in high school, and were considered the "perfect couple." He was the captain of the football team and she was head cheerleader. But in the last few days she had realized she was falling for Sammy.

"Who is it?" she asked.

"Your fiance," he replied.

"Is that you Sammy? Hold on, I'll be there in a minute," she said, frantically shoving her letter in a drawer and scampering to the door. "I was wondering if I was ever going to see you again," she said.

"You knew you would," as he put his hand on her shoulder.

"You're right, I guess I did."

"I've just had a lot on my mind lately," Sammy explained.

"Like what? Sammy, tell me about it."

Setting his other hand on her arm, he gently told her that he was falling in love with her and wanted her to be his wife. She just laughed at him as if he was kidding.

"I love you, Jacki. I mean it. But I know that unless I get out of this business I can't be true to you." Jacki just nodded her head as if she understood the situation.

* * * *

They dated for two years. Sammy concealed his drugs carefully, but she knew at times he was high. She was true to him, but he let her down on the road.

One night he took her to a drive-in movie. But five minutes into the movie Sammy burst out slurring a phrase so badly Jacki couldn't understand what he said.

"What'd you say?"

"I said, I have something for you," handing her a small box. "Will you marry me?"

Tears began to flow down her face and drip onto the leather seats. She studied the ring while pondering what to say. "I guess it's been a long time coming. You know I'll marry you. I love you, Sammy."

"I love you too, Jacki," he said, embracing her with a kiss.

Jacki continued to cry, totally unaware of the chaotic sounds screaming from the window speaker and the action packed scenes flooding the monstrous screen. It was as if the two lovers were on their own island, basking in each other's affection, existing in their own reality.

Sammy held her tightly, her head resting on his shoulder, tears now dampening his sweater.

"Jacki," Sammy wiped the moisture from under her eyes, "What's the matter? Don't you ever smile?"

After dropping Jacki off, Sammy rushed home to tell his folks about the engagement. The living room was the same, the furniture all in place, and the television on. But by the expression on his parents' faces one would have thought they were in mourning. And in a sense they were.

"Sammy, I've got to talk to you," his father said.

"So do I," Sammy said. "I've got great news. I just asked Jacki to marry me."

"Congratulations, Son," his father said in a tone of voice that indicated what he had to say was more important. "I had a dream last night that kept me up all night. It was about you, Sammy."

"Don't stop; go on," Sammy said anxiously.

"Well, in the dream you'd rejected God completely and as a result you died."

Sammy's face tightened as he became angered. Was this just another ploy to get him back into church? "This is getting ridiculous. They're going a little bit too far now," Sammy thought. "It was just a dream, Dad, nothing to get worked up about."

"It was more than just a dream. I love you, Son. That's why I told you about it."

"I know what you believe, but I just can't. I came home thinking you'd be glad to hear about Jacki and me, and all you care about is some meaningless dream."

"Your mother and me are both happy for you, but if something happens to you, marriage isn't going to do you any good."

"Thanks for your concern, Dad," Sammy said sarcastically. "If I die, you can have the Riviera."

Chapter 2

Destiny of Despair

One evening two guys, obviously homosexuals, began dancing with one another, and Sammy and the group started laughing at them and making comments to each other. Evidently a friend of the two dancers didn't appreciate the group's reaction and started glaring at Sammy with intimidating eyes. Between sets Sammy maneuvered his way through the crowded dance floor to the bathroom to comb his hair. The angered customer followed him inside. As Sammy turned the corner to leave, a fist was implanted squarely between his eyes, knocking him out cold. When he regained consciousness, and was helped to his feet, his hand brushed through a spill of blood from a gash opened up on his forehead. Forced to take a few days off to recover, he started blaming God for the mishap as he lay in bed one night.

"So God, you've got me where you want me, out of the club, on my back away from everything I have." He figured if God was going to kill him though, the attacker would have had a knife. "Perhaps God is just trying to give me a little scare," Sammy thought.

Several weeks later, during a Birdwatchers' performance, a guy started firing a gun wildly in the air. Women began screaming and others flew out the exits and under tables. Eddie ducked behind his drums, covering his head with a cymbal. The other guys leaped behind the amplifiers. Sammy had nowhere to hide, so he fell on his face, holding tightly to the microphone. He was no longer singing through it, but the audience heard some heavy breathing. The man was finally arrested, and Sammy left the club that night feeling as though he was on God's hit list. "Well, you missed again," he said half seriously, looking up into the sky.

From then on he began to blame God for everything that didn't go his way. He felt God was using cops, his parents, his group, and everything possible to punish him.

As Sammy's hatred toward God mounted he went deeper into alcohol and drugs than he'd ever been before. Some nights he'd get so wasted he couldn't make it home. The jolt of a police officer lifting him from an alley he'd wandered into during the night, or the strange feeling of waking up in an unfamiliar bed became commonplace.

Before one concert he really got loaded and was anxious to let out some of the drug-created energy on the crowd, when he received an urgent call from his brother-in-law in Ocala, Fla. "Sammy, we just got word from the doctors on Jeff," his voice beginning to break, "he's got leukemia."

Instantly Sammy was torn from the grasps of the alcohol. "Oh, God. How bad is it?"

"That's why I'm calling. They said it's terminal and don't give him much time. We were wondering if you could come and see him."

"I'll drive in tomorrow," Sammy said as he started to fight back the tears. After he hung up, he wandered around backstage, hands squeezed inside his pockets, his chin resting against his chest, trying to convince himself that it wasn't true. Sammy's sadness turned to anger as he flung empty beer bottles across the room, scattering particles everywhere, and pounding dents into the wall with clenched fists. Facing the wall, he fell to his knees, sliding his swollen, bleeding knuckles into his armpits to relieve the pain, tears streaming into his opened mouth.

"Please don't die, Jeff! Please don't die," Sammy grimaced.

The face of his little nephew before him, his music that night must have been performed subconsciously, because his thoughts were totally on Jeff. They did all the things most fathers would do with their sons. It was hard for Sammy to imagine that the little boy who used to wrap his arms around his uncle's waist and give him a big hug was now only hugging to his sheets. The face that quite often wore an ice cream mask from his nose to his chin now only wore an expression of fear. His cute giggle had probably turned to silence.

"God, if you wanted to punish me, why punish an innocent little boy? Leave him alone. I'm the one you want. Do what you want to me, just leave him alone," Sammy said, trying to free himself from the guilt he felt for Jeff's illness.

When he walked up to the front of the hospital he glanced up at the third floor, wishing he could fly through Jeff's window as if he were his saviour, here to rescue him from the bonds of sickness. Upon opening the door, the family one by one gave him a hug. Sammy made his way to Jeff's side. Amazingly, Jeff was nothing like what Sammy had expected. He was giggling, smiling and playing with the toys he'd brought from home. They knew he was lying in his deathbed, but Jeff was more occupied with his toy truck.

"Uncle Sammy, what are you doing here?"

"I came to make sure they're taking care of my partner. How ya feelin'?"

"Okay, but when can I go home?"

"Real soon Jeff, real soon. We've got some fishing to do."

Sammy couldn't stay long that night because he had to get back for a concert, but promised to return after the tour was completed.

Throughout the tour, Sammy buried his guilt

by drinking and getting stoned more than he ever had before. He began using drugs he'd never touched. First, he used DMT, a hallucinogenic drug, and later cocaine and morphine. He wanted to help Jeff, but there was nothing he could do. Feeling desperate, driving back to see his nephew, Sammy promised that if God would just make Jeff well, he would serve Him. But not until Jeff was well.

Every chance he had he visited the hospital. One old nurse who reminded him of his librarian in junior high school because of her constant demand for silence, would always run Sammy out of Jeff's room around closing time. She'd point her finger at him and tell him to be quiet. One time she really got bold. "Why don't you get your hair cut? There's probably enough germs in there to start an epidemic. You should be wearing a hair net," she said, although he could never tell if she was really angry. She allowed Sammy to funnel some of the hostility he had for God in her direction.

Hoping to get her back, he brought his guitar into Jeff's room and proceeded to give him some live music. Before long, most of the nurses and some of the patients gathered around to see what was going on. Jeff was laughing, bobbing his head to the music, and waving his hands like the song leader in church did, when Clara, as Sammy called her, made her appearance.

"I should have known. Mr. Hall, get out of here right now. If you want to serenade someone, there's a group of people eating down in the cafeteria who might be polite enough to listen to your noise," she said as she walked away.

"Clara!" Sammy yelled.

"My name's not Clara," she shouted back.

"Whatever. How 'bout singing a duet?" he asked, hoping to get her riled.

She must have caught on to his intentions because she just gave him a phony smile and kept on walking.

His whole life had become a triangle of thoughts: Jeff, God and himself. Time and time again he promised God he would follow Him if He'd only let Jeff live. His guilt continued to mount and drugs seemed to be his only escape.

Looking for some way or someone to soothe his pains, Sammy started talking to a girl at the club who had a reputation for dealing in hard drugs. Jacki was out on a flight, so he gave the girl a ride home. Sitting in the car outside her apartment, she suggested he try some stuff she guaranteed would take all his worries away. It was an hallucinogenic mixed with marijuana. He had tried almost everything else so why not try this too, he figured. Sammy let her out and started north on the interstate from Miami to his home in Ft. Lauderdale. The drugs started playing with Sammy's mind. He'd experimented with all types, but this drug was doing things he'd never experienced. Light posts, cars, and buildings seemed to be passing him so rapidly he thought he was going 100 miles an hour. The speedometer said he was only going twenty. Then in an instant everything seemed to be passing slowly when he was actually going 80 miles per hour. Thoughts began to scramble around in his brain out of control. He no longer had command of his actions. His entire body was draped around the steering wheel, trying to stay on his side of the road but weaving from shoulder to shoulder, sending evading cars into the gravel and bushes on either side. He could feel his body separating into two people. One was on the roof clutching on for life. The other was at the steering wheel trying desperately to avoid collisions, although side-swiping a speed limit sign and nearly missing a hitch-hiker who thought he'd finally gotten a ride only to have to dive into a ditch to avoid the Riviera. Peering in his rearview mirror Sammy could see the kid was okay by the hand signal he was flashing Sammy's way, but the contents of his run-over backpack were strung out all over the highway.

Sammy could feel himself losing touch with reality. He needed to talk to someone, anyone at all. Pulling into a gas station down the road, he approached the attendant. But when Sammy started talking to him the man acted as if Sammy was going to kill him. "What's wrong with you mister? Get away from me!" he said while backing into a gas pump and then sprinting to the office and locking himself inside. Sammy hopped back into his car and with a deep breath started back down the road.

But this time he could sense he wasn't alone. Voices, growling voices, were screaming and yelling his name. "Sammy, Sammy, Sammy," the voices echoed louder and more intense and before he knew it demons were swarming all over him, their slimy hands smearing sweat across his body, sinking piercing fingernails into his skin, clawing at his face, and mingling through his hair. A figure of Satan began to materialize in the seat right next to him, startling Sammy so that for a brief second his hands left the wheel. At first, too stunned to speak, he forced out a cry for help. "Help me, please somebody help me! I can't take it!" He began to scream like a baby, making no words, just terrified sounds.

The satanic figure sat there without saying a word. He was everything that was ugly and fearful. His mere presence brought a sense of death. It was as if the Devil had come to collect Sammy's soul, and he was about to get it. Suddenly Sammy slid over to the side of the road and without turning off the engine or shutting his door, he started running through an open field, trying to escape the horror. He fell down, got up, and then stumbled again. Digging his hands into the dirt he started crawling deeper into the darkness. A loud demanding voice penetrated Sammy's ears, "Take your life, kill yourself." Sammy didn't have the power in himself to refuse the compelling voice. He picked himself off the ground and ran to his car to find a sharp object. He rummaged wildly through the car, but to no avail. He started running for a hamburger restaurant about a quarter-mile back, where he could break into the kitchen and grab a knife. It would be over in minutes. But when he saw a police car pass by, he got back in his car and started driving. The police car evaporated like fog amongst the wind; it had been an hallucination. His foot jammed the accelerator to the floor intending to end it all, but desperately he cried out, "God, please help me. Please God, I need your help. I give up. Please help me!" he repeatedly yelled.

Nothing happened, and voices started taunting Sammy again as the satanic materialization returned. Sammy thought he'd rather die than go through it once more. Again the gas pedal went to the floor, eyes closed, his head buried in the wheel, urging the car to maximum speed, heading for a ditch. "God, I need your help," Sammy begged. "I'm sorry, this time is different, just help me." Instantly a comforting warmth came over him and he was freed from the tormenting spirit which had attempted to collect Sammy's life that night. The car swerved to avoid the ditch, and miraculously made it back onto the pavement. The misery and turmoil Sammy had felt inside for so long was gone. It was replaced with a love and a peace that he had never known before. His tears came from joy, not fear or desperation.

The war was over. Sammy had surrendered to God's love, and as the sun began to rise that morning while driving home, it symbolized a new start for Sammy Hall. He was on his way to rising above his problems. He prayed and rejoiced the whole way home. He was a different person, but suddenly as he passed a bar a couple of blocks from his house a startling thought crossed his mind. "What about the club and my career?" he wondered. But the peace he had in his heart took away any worries, and he went to bed that night free from the grasps of an unhappy world.

Chapter 3

Breaking Away

The singing of birds outside Sammy's window woke him earlier than usual the next morning. He could see them lifting their beaks and whistling as if they didn't have a care in the world. The sky was clear, seemingly invisible, and only in contrast to the green trees was its deep blue shade revealed. The wind was enough to blow falling leaves from their course, yet unable to move them once they'd reached the ground. Birds continued to chorus until a barking dog sent them soaring for the top of the sky, settling instead for a housetop or distant tree.

It was only 8:30, and he'd only had several hours sleep, but the confusion in the next room from his family getting ready for church made sleep impossible. After lying there for about 15 minutes, his head under the covers, his pillow fallen to the floor, he realized it was hopeless. Sammy was wide awake and well rested, and for the first time in years he actually wanted to go to church.

Occasionally, in the past, he dropped in for a church service just to keep his parents happy. Usually he'd wear a pair of Levi's and a nice shirt, but that morning he felt like a changed person and wanted to look different too; so he pulled out a suit he'd bought for a buddy's wedding.

When he walked into the service they were in the middle of a hymn. It was a good thing the organist knew what she was playing because she eyed Sammy all the way to his seat, paying little attention to the music in front of her. The song-leader himself gave a smile in Sammy's direction, while the minister was preoccupied doing some last minute studying of his sermon notes. One by one heads turned to inspect Sammy. Most likely they were more astonished he was wearing a suit than the fact that he was there. And when he didn't sit in the back row as usual, some wondered if this was the same guy they'd prayed for all these years.

As far as Sammy could see, the church was still the same. In particular, the 'three blind mice' as Sammy called them, were still sitting next to each other in the second row on the right side. They were three older ladies who would grab Sammy by the arm and tell him God loved him. No matter what tactic he used to avoid them, they always found him. Sometimes he'd sneak out during the closing prayer or hide in the bathroom till the coast was clear, but nothing worked. One of the three would always ambush him. At times he wondered if God had given them supernatural powers.

Mrs. Miller, the most successful "hunter" of the three, would always shout "Thank you, Jesus!" every time the pastor raised his voice. Her record was 21 "Thank you, Jesus'!" in one service. Then there was Mrs. Mazzilli, an elderly Italian woman that stood up every time the minister gave the congregation a chance to say what God had done for them. Sammy would usually time her. Five minutes was considered a short sermon for her, and there were times she'd go on and on and the pastor would begin saying "amen" to try to stop her. The third woman loved to sing. She sang off-key, but that didn't stop her from drowning out most of the congregation. Everyone called her "Gramma Nelson." One time she got up to sing a solo, and sang so loud into the microphone that everyone put their fingers in their ears for protection.

Usually Sammy would spend his time in church jotting down lyrics for songs to use in his act and thinking about anything other than what was being preached. But that morning he listened intently, and several words stuck in his mind: "Whatever talents you have, God has given you. And He expects you to use them for His glory." Sammy prayed quietly to himself while the minister continued. "Lord, whatever you want me to do, I'll do it. Please God, show me how I can use my music for you," he asked, hoping God would allow him to stay in the club.

After the service was over he rushed to his car. But just as the key turned to unlock his door, he heard someone yell his name. Sure enough, the three ladies were hot on his trail, their purses dangling from their arms, one hand holding onto their hats to keep them from blowing off. They looked like three kids chasing after an ice cream truck.

"Sammy, it's good to see you. You sure look handsome this morning," Mrs. Miller said, referring to his suit.

"Thank you Mrs. Miller," he muttered dryly.

"We're still praying for you every day," Mrs. Mazzilli added.

"Thank you; I need it."

"Someday Sammy, you're going to be used by God in a mighty way. Just wait and see," Mrs. Miller predicted.

"He's going to be a singer for Jesus," Gramma Nelson offered.

"You never know," Sammy said, amusingly thinking to himself 'if they only knew,' but knowing he needed to make some decisions with his career before he told anyone. "I've got to run, ladies," he said, leaving in a hurry.

Around the table that afternoon he knew his parents were wondering what prompted him to go to church, and especially why he wore a suit. But Sammy, although dying to tell them what they'd waited to hear for years, knew he had some things to settle first. He knew how they would respond, but he was worried about what

Jacki would say.

The group had two performances that night. One was a concert and the other was their usual show at the club. It was an uncomfortable situation for Sammy. Here he was feeling so great inside and singing one of the group's newest hits *Weeping Analeah,* a song about drugs. Sammy realized he couldn't sing these types of songs and share God too. He had to leave the group. If he stayed, he knew his happiness wouldn't last.

The kids were really getting turned on to the music that night, but every note brought Sammy more discomfort. The thrill of being on stage and having thousands scream his name no longer brought him excitement.

Later at the club, after the second show, sitting on a stool in the corner of his dressing room with his face buried in his hands, Sammy prayed for the courage to leave the group. He didn't have another job, a high school diploma, or the skills to guarantee work. Nonetheless, he knew he had to get out.

The band knew something was going on with Sammy, because he hadn't gotten loaded the last few days. Instead he sat by himself trying to deal with the struggle he was feeling inside. Then his chance to leave the group came. A couple of the guys got into an argument about expenses and before long the whole band was in a fight. Chairs were flying and windows were breaking, it's a wonder no one was seriously injured. It was a typical barroom brawl. Except for a few bruises and cuts the group was still intact. When it was all over, Sammy announced he was leaving the group.

"I can't put up with this stuff anymore," Sammy said angrily. "I quit."

"Come on, we were just letting out some of our tension. There's no harm done," Joey, the lead guitarist said.

"It's not only the fight, I just need a change."

Bobby spoke up, "I understand, man, but why don't you think about it some more? Let's leave him alone guys," as he motioned them to the door.

Leaning against the wall in the midst of a jungle of dressing room furniture, his stool crushed next to his feet, Sammy thought about what he was giving up. But his mind flashed back to that night in the car, and his doubts quickly disappeared.

Just then Bobby came in. "Sammy I think we'd better pump up the amps and start rockin' a little," he said before noticing that Sammy was staring motionless at the ground. "What's wrong with you?" he asked.

"I'm just tired."

"Here, take a couple of shots of this, it'll wake you up," as he handed him a bottle.

"That's not what I mean, I'm tired of the group. I'm serious man, I can't go on any longer."

"All the guys have those days when they get

sick of the same old thing, but it passes. Just hang in there," Bobby said, trying to ignore Sammy's decision. "I really think we'd better jack up the amps though, I just heard a customer say we belong on Lawrence Welk. Come on, man, show them what you've got."

"I'm not going on, Bobby."

"What do ya mean you're not going on? We've got to be out there in five minutes!"

"I'm through, Bobby."

"OK, OK," Bobby replied, lifting his hands as if he was surrendering. "I'm not going to press it, but think about it some more tonight and give us your final decision tomorrow at rehearsal. I'll just tell everyone you got sick and had to go home."

Nonetheless, he was certain he was leaving the group and felt free to tell everyone about his experience. Sammy drove over to Jacki's apartment, still afraid of what she was going to say and not sure how he was going to tell her. He knew she would be asleep, but he couldn't wait.

After pounding on her door for a few minutes, he woke up Jacki and the rest of the floor with her, including a woman across the hall.

"What's wrong with you, banging on doors this time of night? Kids don't have any respect these days," she said through the crack in her door.

"I'm sorry, ma'am, but this is an emergency."

"Oh, is there anything I can do?" she asked.

"Yeah, help me knock." She proceeded to

bang along with Sammy until Jacki opened the door. There she stood leaning on the knob as if it was the only thing holding her up.

"Thanks for your help ma'am," Sammy said as he closed the door behind him and led Jacki to the couch. "Jacki, I've got something important to tell you. Are you awake?"

Before she could answer, someone knocked on the door. "Is there anything else I can do?" the neighbor asked.

"No, I think I've got things under control."

"Well, what's the emergency anyway?" she frowned.

"I shouldn't tell you this," Sammy said, motioning her to come closer, "but since you helped me it'll be OK. Just don't tell anybody. OK? You promise?"

"Sure! What is it?" she asked impatiently.

"Now you're sure I can trust you?" Sammy continued, trying to think of a reason.

"Come on, what is it?"

"She's a secret agent for the CIA and I'm here to protect her," Sammy whispered in her ear.

"Wow," the lady exclaimed, "she doesn't look like a secret agent."

"Neither do I, but that's what makes us effective. Listen, if you want to help your country, you'll go to bed and keep quiet."

When Sammy made it back to the couch, Jacki was half asleep. "Jacki? Wake up. Are you awake?"

"Uh-huh," she answered, "this better be important."

"I've accepted Jesus Christ into my life, and I'm quitting the Birdwatchers."

"What?"

"I'm not exactly sure what happened myself, except that the Devil or something tried to make me kill myself."

"What are you talking about?" Jacki glared back.

"The other night I was really down about Jeff, and I was missing you, so I took some 'special' grass to relax a little. It sent me soaring. And before long, I don't know what they were: demons, spirits, something, but they began swarming all over me, ordering me to kill myself," Sammy explained.

Jacki opened her eyes widely and closed them again several times, making sure it wasn't all a dream.

"You believe me, don't you Jacki?"

"So then what happened?" she asked, avoiding the question.

"Well, I know this sounds incredible, but it really happened. A figure of Satan appeared right beside me, and I remember jamming on the gas, trying to kill myself," Sammy said. "But I cried out for God's help, and instantly the effect of the drug left, and the spirits disappeared."

"Listen Sammy, it was probably just an hallucination. Drugs can do that, ya know. Besides, what does this have to do with leaving the group?"

"It wasn't an hallucination. It was real. Don't you see. God saved my life. I owe Him everything. I know He isn't happy with the life I've been living," Sammy declared. "And I won't be happy unless I get out of the group and start serving God. Don't you understand?"

"No, I don't. It was just the drugs playing with your mind, and you're blowing it all out of proportion. You're going to ruin your whole life just because of one bad trip," she cried angrily.

"Believe me, Jacki."

"Believe you nothin'. Just leave me alone," she shouted, tears flowing past the weary rings under her eyes.

Sammy left that night fearing Jacki was going to leave him, but worse, wondering if he was destined to return to those little old churches with their numerous flaws. "I know you're real, Jesus," Sammy said looking skyward, "but do I have to choose between stardom and drugs and the pulpit and those Sunday morning hypocrites? There's got to be something better. Please Lord, show me where it is."

The following morning he told his mom he had given his life to Christ and was no longer a member of the Birdwatchers. She cried and cried before she could even say a word. She hugged him tightly and began using one of Mrs. Miller's lines. "Thank you, Jesus, thank you, Jesus," she repeated. After her tears were almost gone she started calling all his brothers and sisters and people at church. Every time she'd start to tell someone about it she'd start crying again. Meanwhile, Sammy went and told his dad at the grocery store. His dad was also excited, and for the first time in years he flipped Sammy a peach off the fruit stand and they sat eating together, both smiling and dripping juice onto the floor.

Sammy knew he had to let Bobby know his decision was final. As he was walking toward the stage, Bobby came from a side door.

"The star has arrived!" Bobby said. "I've got great news. I got a call from Billboard Magazine this morning and they want to do a full spread feature on 'Sammy Hall, the Rising Star.' "

"I'm sorry Bobby, it doesn't matter," Sammy said. "I'm still leaving the group."

"You're crazy! You're on the verge of making it to the top, and you're throwing it all away," he said.

"It's something I have to do," Sammy explained.

"I don't know why, but I knew you'd made up your mind last night. Do us a favor and play out a two week notice, so we can find another lead singer."

Sammy agreed to do it, but came down with laryngitis which prevented him from performing.

That afternoon he went up to see Jeff. His health was getting worse as time went on, but Sammy knew Jeff was going to get better now that he had surrendered his life to Christ. "God isn't going to punish me any longer," Sammy thought.

"Jeff, my man, how ya doin'?"

"Not too bad," he said weakly, straining to keep his eyes open.

"I came here to tell you that I know you're going to get better. I promise. God's going to make you well."

Recovering in bed that week from his throat problems, Sammy spent a lot of time praying for Jacki, Jeff, and for God to help him get out of his contracts. Sammy had several solo releases with a record company that also had Tom Jones and Engelbert Humperdinck under contract. He didn't want to keep recording, but a contract was more binding than his work with the Birdwatchers. He wasn't sure he could back out on them.

Jacki didn't visit him while he was sick, and his attempts to reach her by phone despite his raspy voice were unsuccessful. He asked himself if she was going to call off their wedding, which was to take place in two weeks. Finally, her girlfriend answered the phone. "Sorry, she's out with an old friend from school," she said. His heart was broken. "Dear God, don't take her from me," he begged.

The next day she came and saw him. Sure enough, she was out with her old boyfriend, but realized that she was still in love with Sammy. Before she left she caressed his head and gave him a kiss like never before, disregarding his sickness.

The next Sunday Sammy took Jacki to church. The pastor was real emotional, waving his arms, whipping off his coat, and wiping perspiration from his forehead as he skipped across the stage. Sammy knew Jacki was feeling uncomfortable. The minister reminded her of the preachers she had seen on TV who shouted loudly, getting the people all fired up before taking their money. This preacher was a phony too, she thought. When they got to the car she couldn't hold back her tears.

"I'm not going back into that church ever again. It's just not for me. You can go there all you want, but don't expect me to come with you." She continued to cry while Sammy tried to comfort her.

The night before the wedding some of his friends had a party for him. Drugs and alcohol were being passed around, but Sammy stayed clear. Until later in the evening a friend convinced him to take just a few last "hits" on some marijuana. Three tokes made Sammy feel like he'd just smoked a dozen joints. He knew he had to get out of there, and feared he'd made God angry again. It wore off before he got home, and he rushed to his room to pour out his guilt for what he'd done, but waiting for him were his family and the three older ladies.

"How was the party, son?" his mother asked.

"Just fine, it's good to see you ladies. What's the occasion?"

"Well, Sammy, we wanted to give you something special for your wedding. This is for you," Mrs. Miller said, handing him an envelope. Inside was a gift certificate from a clothing store in town. "We liked the way you looked in a suit so much that we decided to buy you one. There should be enough there to cover it."

"Thanks a lot ladies, it seems the only time I buy a suit is before weddings," Sammy laughed.

"Don't you think Sammy would look better if he got his hair cut before the ceremony?" his mother suggested.

Simultaneously, the three ladies agreed. "You're no longer a rock and roll star, you're a Christian. Christians aren't supposed to have long hair," Mrs. Mazzilli said.

"Where in the Bible does it say I have to have my hair a certain length?" Sammy asked. "Jesus doesn't care about my hair. He looks at our attitudes and actions, not the length of our hair."

Mrs. Miller answered, "It doesn't come right out and say it, but it says we're supposed to be separate from the world. Even though you've changed inside, the only thing people can see is you and your long hair."

"What do you think Dad?" Sammy asked.

"I think you should get it cut, Sammy. But it's up to you. We can't force you to do it," his father said.

The next morning he had it cut. The barber turned what was supposed to be a "trim" into a "butch". He must have taken out his frustration over the younger generation's hairstyles on Sammy. Sammy left not knowing whether to hit the barber or have him do a quick hair weave. He looked more like a World War II veteran than a rock and roll idol.

Whispers flooded the crowd as Sammy and his attendants made their way to the front of the church to await their respective bridesmaids marching down the center aisle. The audience caught sight of Sammy's haircut and was trying to hold in their snickering. One by one the bridesmaids became bright eyed as they saw him.

Jacki was noticeably upset. "What have you done to yourself?" she said under her breath. Sammy wondered if she was crying because of his hair or because she was so happy.

On their way to the hotel she didn't look at him. "Talk to me, Jacki. What's wrong?" Sammy asked.

"You know what's wrong, don't talk to me," she said angrily.

"It's only my hair. I'm sorry. Please forgive me."

"Just don't talk to me," she pouted.

Laying on the bed, her face smothered in a pillow, weeping desperately, Sammy tried to console her. "Jacki, I love you. Please talk to me."

"How could you cut your hair off like that?" she demanded loudly.

"I didn't want to, but they made me do it."

"What do you mean, 'they made you do it'?"

"Some old ladies in the church talked me into it. They said God didn't approve of my long hair."

"So now you're Mr. Spiritual! If that's what your God makes you do, I don't want any part of it," she replied.

"My God isn't that way. He doesn't order us around. He's loving and caring. Don't worry, it'll grow back. Look at me, Jacki. Do you still love me?"

Lifting her head and looking into his concerned eyes she said, "You know I do, I just was taken by surprise. I thought I was marrying Sammy Hall and you don't resemble him at all," she said sadly.

"I'm sorry," he said as he snuggled up beside her on the bed. "What's the matter? Don't you ever smile?" Sammy said, causing a grin to appear on her tear moistened face.

By the time the honeymoon was over, Sammy was still struggling over his contract commitments. These were powerful people and he didn't want to rub them the wrong way. Finally, he knew he had to do something. "Oh God," Sammy prayed before walking in, "give me the boldness to go through with it."

Upon walking into the producer's office, a place where months earlier he had signed contracts which were inevitably going to take him to the top, his throat tightened.

"Have a seat, son," the man motioned, as two agents sat stationary on the couch flanked by plantholders. "What can I do for you?"

"I guess I'll not waste your time," Sammy said, adjusting the sunglasses propped up on his head; "I'll get right to the point. I only want to record gospel music from now on."

The two other men laughed openly; meanwhile a grin came to the producer's face. "You've got to be kidding."

"No, I'm quite serious."

"Nobody buys religious records. What do you want to sing, *Jesus Loves Me*?" he teased. "You can't make any money singing that stuff."

"I just want to sing gospel music, that's all."

"I don't care what you want. We'll tell you what we want," he said angrily, rising from behind his desk. "We're going to make you a superstar. Don't you want that?"

"I do, but I just can't sing that same old stuff anymore. I just can't," Sammy frowned.

"Well, we're not going to produce an album of Sunday school choruses," he said, "so you can consider yourself no longer under contract with us."

When he turned to leave, one of the agents handed Sammy his card. "When you come to your senses kid, give me a call."

"That's why I'm here," Sammy responded. "I came to my senses."

Chapter 4

Do It Your Way

"Hey, aren't you Sammy Hall the singer?" the kid asked, as Sammy carried in the new, deep shag carpet.

"That's right."

"What are you doin' puttin' in carpet? You must make lots of bucks from your concerts."

"I'm not singing anymore," Sammy said. "I've given it up."

"Well, why?" the boy asked strangely.

"I just got tired of it, that's all."

"I was one of your biggest fans. I've got all your albums, and a scrapbook with all your clippings."

"That's real nice, thanks; but I'd better get back to work," Sammy said embarrassingly. So here he was, a celebrity who once made as much money as he needed, making $60 a week, laying carpet for his brother-in-law.

Then, adding to his humiliation, he overheard his young fan on the phone. "Guess who's laying carpet at my house? Sammy Hall! He's dressed in old beat-up overalls and everything. His hair's all cut off too. Grab Johnny and get over here right away. You won't believe it."

Kids who had at one time idolized him were now making fun of him.

Occasionally, on the weekends, he would sing in churches around the area, but he wanted more chances for ministry. Sammy knew he didn't want to be a carpet-layer the rest of his life. Eventually he was asked to take on an entire service in Hollywood, Florida. It was a small church of about 50 people, but one would have thought it was a congregation of 50,000 seeing how nervous Sammy was. He didn't have to worry about the church's sound system. They didn't have one. Nor did he have to worry about being heard, since everyone could fit in the first four rows. The last few rows were seemingly set aside as a nursery area for mothers with crying babies, and they cried as loud as Sammy sang. He didn't say more than a few words throughout the entire service, because he was so afraid of not being accepted.

As more bookings came, it was getting easier for him, but deep down Sammy didn't feel comfortable singing the old traditional songs. People were telling him he had to sing songs from the 1800's, preach like Jimmy Swaggart, and dress more like an undertaker. And Sammy felt like he was becoming something he wasn't.

Amazingly, the offers to lure him back into

the rock and roll industry kept pouring in, while he became more dissatisfied with his style of ministry. As far as Sammy was concerned, Jacki still didn't understand why he had given up all he had; the job was getting harder every day, and the wages were as low as ever.

Driving home from work one day he decided to go by the club to see if any of the guys in the group were around. Sammy caught them in the middle of a rehearsal. Standing just inside the back door, shielded by the darkness, he saw their new lead singer doing some of his old songs. His discouragement and temptation to return mounted. He could envision himself back on stage soaking in applause, lifting their spirits, standing before the crowd of worshippers. He wondered if he had made a mistake getting out of his record contracts, pulling the agent's card from his wallet to consider giving him a call. But once the group had finished the song, the memories of drunken bodies slumped over tables, smoke irritating his eyes, and women throwing themselves at him, made him sick. He left without letting the guys know he was there, feeling confused.

A few months earlier, Sammy had developed a growth on his eye, and after surgery it still didn't improve. In fact, it was growing steadily worse. It was discovered that the growth had come back, and he was scheduled for surgery the next morning.

Lying in bed, the lights long since turned out, neither Sammy nor Jacki could get to sleep.

"Sammy!" Jacki asked, "are you awake?"

"Yeah; wide awake," he over-pronounced.

"I'm scared, honey. I don't know what I'd do without you."

"I'm scared too, but the people at church prayed for me tonight after the service that God would heal me. I know He can do it," Sammy assured her.

"Those things don't really happen, Sammy," she said.

"Sure they do, if we believe strong enough. Jacki, promise me one thing, that you'll call the pastor and have him pray while I'm in surgery tomorrow."

"C'mon Sammy, I don't want to talk to him."

"Please Jacki; please."

"Okay, all right," she finally agreed.

Jacki was panicking inside. "What if it's cancer. I can't live without Sammy. "God," she said to herself, "if you make Sammy well, you've got another believer."

The next morning Sammy came running from the bathroom. "Jacki! Jacki!" Sammy screamed. "It's gone. The growth is gone. Praise the Lord."

Jacki's eyes got big, as the plate in her trembling hand slipped onto the table. "Let me see," feeling for herself. She began to thank God herself, and accepted God at Sammy's next service. So many times Sammy wished he could have picked her up out of her pew and carried her down to the altar. But it wasn't necessary; she came on her own.

Things seemed to be getting better for Sammy. His wife had accepted the Lord, his eye was restored, his son Monte was born, he'd gotten a more enjoyable and higher paying job as a carpenter, and he was getting greater opportunities to sing. But then disaster struck.

One morning Jeff woke up and told the nurses everything was blurry. According to the doctors, Jeff was going blind, and in just several weeks he had totally lost his sight.

It crushed Sammy to see Jeff in this condition, but he knew he had to keep his pal in good spirits.

"I'm back," Sammy said, grabbing Jeff's hand for the customary handshake. "How's it goin', buddy?"

"OK I just wish I could see you again, Uncle Sammy."

"Don't worry, you will," biting on his lip to keep from noticeably crying.

"I know," Jeff replied. "The lights have just gone out. When they come back on, I'll see again."

"That's right, God will turn the lights on real soon, so hang in there," Sammy paused to regain his composure. "Oh! I brought you a gift."

"What is it?"

"Guess!" placing it into Jeff's hand.

"Oh, wow! My very own wallet! Thanks a lot."

"*See!* It's got a place to put your pictures, and everything," Sammy said, failing to catch himself before he realized what he had said. From then on, Jeff slept with it under his pillow.

In the next several months Jeff's condition seemed to improve, and the doctors believed the disease had gone into remission. Even though Jeff was released from the hospital his hair continued to fall out and his frail body was the picture of weakness.

One afternoon the family gathered together at Sammy's for lunch. Jeff sat in front of Sammy on the mini-bike as they sped around and around in the backyard, dogs chasing after them untiringly.

"OK mister," Jeff ordered, turning his head back at Sammy. "You're under arrest; pull over!"

"Yes sir," Sammy replied, stopping the bike. "What seems to be the problem, officer?"

"You just ran three stop signs and barely missed an old lady. Besides that, you've been going 50 in a 30 mph zone."

"I'm sorry, sir; please don't give me a ticket."

"A ticket? You're going to jail."

"Oh no I'm not," Sammy grinned, taking off again around the yard, Jeff screaming for him to stop.

The day of fun and games was over as Jeff slept motionless on the couch, his hands tucked under his head to serve as a pillow. Jeff was so exhausted Sammy had to carry him to the car, laying him gently in the backseat.

Little did Sammy know he would be crawling in that backseat once again later that night.

"Sammy! Wake up," Jacki whispered in his ear. "Sammy, Sammy," she nudged him.

"What's the matter?" he said hoarsely.

"Someone's banging on the door."

"What time is it," he asked, trying to focus his eyes on the alarm clock. "2:30! Who could it be?"

"I don't know. Be careful," Jacki said as Sammy walked out.

"Who is it?" Sammy asked, his ear up against the door.

"It's Vonceil," she said frantically.

"What's the matter, sis?"

"It's Jeff; he's real bad. We're on our way to the hospital."

Sammy ran past her before she could even finish her sentence.

"Jeff, my man, you're not feeling too good, huh?"

His pale face shook back and forth slightly.

"Sammy, can I have a Coke?" Jeff asked. "I'm burning up."

Jeff's desire to live seemed to be gone. The pain was just too great.

"Here, Jeff," Sammy lifted his head from the seat, feeling the sweat behind his neck. "Sip it slowly, that's it."

"We'd better go," Vonceil said.

"OK buddy, take care and I love you," Sammy said, kissing his cheek. But Jeff didn't have the strength to respond. As the car sped away, Sammy stared down the road long after the car was out of sight, trying to bring it back. Somehow Sammy knew he would never see his nephew again.

Sleep was impossible that night as they tried to keep in close contact with Sammy's sister at the hospital. A little after 9:00 the phone rang. Sammy and Jacki looked inside each other, knowing the other's fears. Could it be the call they were afraid of?

"Hello," Jacki answered softly. "Oh no," she responded after a short pause.

Immediately Sammy knew Jeff's struggle was over. Sitting at the kitchen table, his face buried in his arms, Sammy couldn't hold back his emotions. Jacki shed tears as well as she stood behind Sammy, her arms wrapped around his head.

"His temperature went up to 108 degrees before he died, but Vonceil said he wasn't in much pain. Sammy, he's better off. He's not suffering anymore."

Sammy continued to cry, but he knew Jacki was right. "At least the lights are on again for Jeff," he thought.

During Jeff's funeral people were crying with their heads bowed, but Sammy was rejoicing. He pictured his little nephew sitting next to God up in heaven, free from leukemia and able to play like he hadn't for so long. He sang Jeff's favorite song, *It's Such a Pretty World,* and as he passed by the coffin for the last time he set two of his albums, including one he'd dedicated to Jeff, on his chest and tucked the wallet under his folded hands.

As time went on, Sammy was getting more invitations than he could handle. Meanwhile, his sisters and their husbands had begun to sing back-up and accompany Sammy during his crusades. But it became evident that it was impossible to hold down their regular jobs and do all the traveling the ministry required. They all quit their jobs and decided to go at it full-time. Sammy's ministry was now spanning the entire east coast, so a more centralized home made sense. They put their houses up for sale and moved to Charlotte, North Carolina.

But Charlotte didn't offer the conveniences that he'd had at home. He found himself living in a small trailer in a park owned by the "Church of God" denomination. The trailer was barely large enough to squeeze two people into, let alone live in. The cramped living conditions, his disgust with the way people were treating him and his wife, and his discontent with his traditional style of ministry continued to make life unbearable.

"I'm sick of this, Jacki," Sammy said. "I'm goin' to the woods until God speaks to me. God doesn't want us waking up hungry and not having enough food to fix for breakfast. And these people have no right to tell us how to act or dress, either."

"Settle down," Jacki said.

"I won't settle down, I know God doesn't want us living like this. We'd be better off on welfare. I'll tell you, I'm gonna stay out there in those woods for days if I have to until He gives me some answers," Sammy pointed through the window.

"When are you going?" Jacki asked.

"I don't know, but I'm going." Sammy paused, "This is enough to make a guy go back into the music business," thinking of how hundreds of kids shoved their way through crowds to touch him and attack his clothes. The only thing that attacked him now were thousands of mosquitoes.

"You're getting excited Sammy, relax," Jacki declared.

"I know, Honey, but God's got to show me what He wants me to do, because I can't go on being what other people think I should be. I want to be myself. There are millions of unsaved kids out there who aren't being reached while we mostly entertain 'warmed-over' Christians."

"I understand," she said. "Several women in the camp came by today and said I've got to start dressing like the rest of them. They said they weren't the only ones who felt that way, too."

"Who were they?" Sammy asked angrily. "I'm going to tell them to mind their own business."

"Don't bother. I already did," she said.

The pressures didn't stop. After one of his crusades in Anniston, Alabama, a woman came up to him. "I'm sorry to hear about your wife; I'll pray for her."

"What do you mean?" Sammy asked. "What's wrong with her?"

"You know, her drug problem."

"What are you talking about?" he frowned.

"I heard your wife is strung out on drugs."

"Tell whoever told you that, that my wife is home right now taking care of our son. She's given her heart to the Lord, and she's not strung out on drugs." And to himself, "That does it! When I get home, I'm headin' for the woods."

But when he got back he didn't have the time to go on his journey; he was to be off in a few days for another series of crusades. "Jacki, I'm back," Sammy yelled from outside the trailer. "Jacki, are you here?"

"I'm over here!" she yelled from another trailer. "I'll be there in a minute." When she returned, she was carrying Monte and a half gallon of milk.

"Where'd you get the milk?" Sammy asked.

"From the Stevens'. They'd seen Monte with water in his bottle for so long I guess they felt sorry for us."

"All that is going to change," Sammy said

sternly. "I'm going to find me a spot tomorrow where God and me can do some talking. And I'm not coming back until I get some answers."

"I thought you were supposed to be in Atlanta the day after tomorrow," Jacki said.

"I know, but I've got to know God's will before I can do any more crusades. If I'm not back by tomorrow night, go ahead and cancel. I may be out there a while."

The next morning, his Bible tucked under his arm, and a blanket to keep him warm at night, he determinedly marched toward his unknown destination. He didn't know exactly what kind of spot he was looking for, but he'd know it when he saw it. Admiring God's creation as he fought his way through the high bush and stumbled through moss-covered streams, Sammy started talking to God.

"Dear God, you know how I've struggled these last few years trying to do your will, but I can't go on unless you give me some answers," Sammy repeated his plea over and over again.

He'd been hiking for several hours when one of the streams he'd been following dove off a cliff into a pond like one only fantasizes about. The water was so clear, and there wasn't a mosquito in sight. Sammy felt like an explorer discovering a new land. Most of all, he wanted to discover God's will.

Making his way around the pond, he spread his blanket in a clearing between three trees and lay on his back gazing through the pines, frequently being blinded by the afternoon sun. Below his feet the pond lay quietly except for the sound of water from the stream crashing down into the pool.

"Well God, this is the place. Here I am all by myself, no food or nothin'. I'm willing to wait as long as it takes. I'll starve to death before I'll leave here without hearing from you," he said, envisioning himself wrapped in his blanket in total darkness, his head laying on his Bible while his stomach rumbled with hunger. "I feel this music in my bones. I know kids like it, and I know some say it's the Devil's music, but God, I know I can reach people with it."

Sammy sat there waiting for a loud voice to speak from above the clouds, but nothing happened. He became more impatient. "God, do something, show me that you're there. Part the pond. Anything! Just do something."

But again nothing happened, so Sammy figured this was going to be a long stay. He opened his Bible anywhere, because he figured he was going to get a chance to read many scriptures. Suddenly his eyes were fixed on one verse from the page he'd turned to at random. "*I am writing these things to you about those who are trying to lead you astray. As for you, the anointing you received from Him remains in you, and you do not need anyone to teach you. But as His anointing teaches you about all things and as that anointing is real, not counterfeit—just as it has taught you, remain in*

Him" (NIV).

"Oh, thank you, Lord," Sammy began to cry. After a while of prayer Sammy started wondering if reading that verse was just a coincidence.

"God, does this mean I can minister the way I feel is right? Can I depend on my gut feelings?" A peace like he'd felt that night when he gave his life to Christ came over him once again. It was as if God was responding to his doubts.

"My Spirit will guide you; don't listen to anyone else," Sammy heard God whisper to his heart.

Tears started flowing again. "But God, I'm going to be ridiculed and put down. My parents won't understand, and the church won't like my contemporary music. Are you sure it will be okay?"

Again God comforted him, "You've known all along what you should be doing; why are you so surprised?"

Sammy lay there basking in the freedom God had given him. "What is Jacki going to think? I've only been out here about three hours," Sammy thought. It was hard for him to believe he'd gotten an answer so soon without having to suffer through the chills of night and a crying stomach.

Running, he hurried back to tell Jacki what had happened. No telling how many miles he'd hiked, but he was able to run all the way back to camp, paying no attention to the mud, water, and vegetation below his feet.

"Jacki!" Sammy shouted. She could see him running across the field. "Jacki!"

As she opened the trailer door she was greeted by a man who had her husband's Bible and blanket, but she wasn't sure it was him because he was disguised with dirt and mud.

"Look at you, Sammy. Did you and God have a wrestling match or something? You're a mess!" she said.

Sammy pulled her from the trailer and pressing her to his mud-coated shirt he started swinging her around. "He spoke to me! God actually spoke to me! I'm free. I'm free at last!"

"What are you talking about? Free from what?" she asked, looking at him peculiarly.

"God spoke to me! Isn't it great?" he exclaimed.

"Will you please put me down? I'm getting dizzy," she pleaded. "Now, tell me what happened."

"God told me it was all right to sing my own way. I'm no longer going to be your typical preacher, and you aren't going to be the everyday preacher's wife who wears dresses from the 1940's and casts stones at women wearing make-up and jewelry."

"We're going to make a lot of people mad," Jacki sighed.

"Who cares?" Sammy scoffed. "As long as it's okay with the Lord, I don't care what anybody else thinks. From now on me and God make the decisions. God can speak to me just as much as anyone else."

"Are you still going to Atlanta?" Jacki inquired.

"You bet. Boy, are they in for a treat! Tomorrow the new Sammy Hall is going to be unveiled. Wait and see, Jacki; God is going to touch more lives through our ministry than ever before."

"I believe it," she agreed.

"And another thing. You're not going to have to live like this much longer. As we totally depend on God, and seek to please Him rather than people, I know we're going to prosper," he said as he started to walk away.

"Where are you going?" she asked.

"I've got to tell the rest of the group about it."

"Well, don't tell them they're looking at the new Sammy Hall, because the way you look, they'll want the old, clean Sammy Hall back."

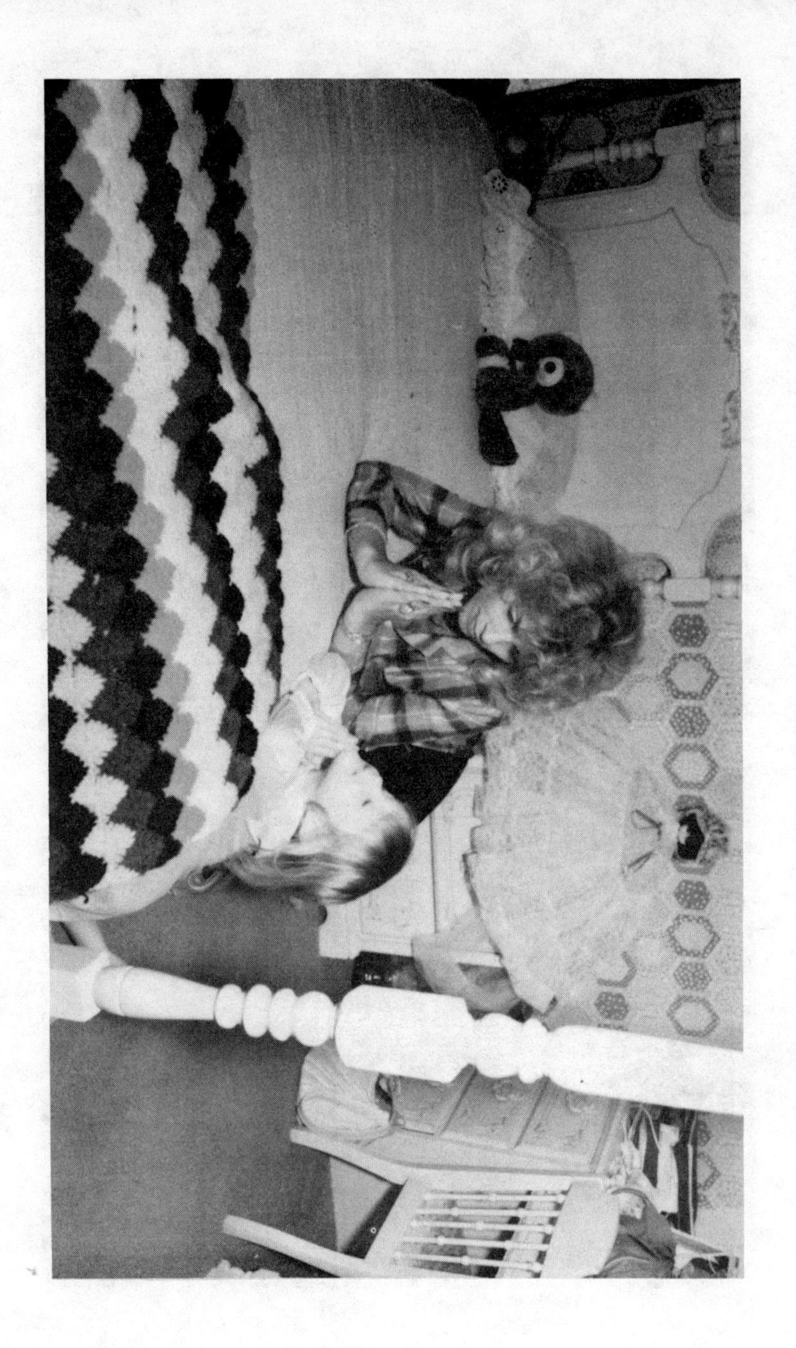

Chapter 5

Our Way—Or Else!

The sounds of jamming guitars, banging drums and echoing voices still vibrated in the background as Sammy asked those who wanted to meet Jesus Christ to come forward. Instantaneously, emptying folding chairs rattled, bleachers swayed, heels snapped against the hard wooden floor as hundreds made their way toward the stage in Billy Graham Crusade style. Unlike his days as a Birdwatcher, the crowd wasn't stomping over one another in hopes of touching Sammy. Instead, they were anxiously scooting down the narrow aisles to dedicate their lives to someone Sammy had introduced as "his closest friend"—Jesus Christ. There seemed to be more people moving from their seats than those remaining. They came from all over the complex, surrounding the platform, squeezing tightly together so others could get closer, yet many had to stand in distant passageways for lack of room. Some heads were bowed, eyes closed, others looked skyward in awe of the moment's magnitude.

Standing before them, reciprocating their tears with his own, Sammy paused to thank God for touching so many lives. "I know how hard it was for some of you to make that walk from your seat," Sammy said, "in front of your friends, all the way up here. Well, another man made a similar walk 2,000 years ago. Except things were a little bit more difficult for him. He had to carry a heavy cross on his back, and people mocked, tormented and spit on him as he made his journey. But his pilgrimage ended in his death, the crucifixion. They nailed him to that cross and drove a spear in his side. Your walk to this stage, though, is going to bring you new life. If you choose to dedicate your life to Christ, you'll never be the same."

After speaking and praying with the gathering a little longer, Sammy dismissed them and started to make his way backstage.

"Hey, Sammy!" a young man shouted, his head peeking above the stage, his arm stretching an album in Sammy's direction. "Will you sign this?"

Sammy grabbed it, thinking it was one of his gospel releases only to realize it was a Birdwatchers' album. Hesitatingly, pulling it closer for inspection, Sammy puzzlingly glanced at the autograph-seeker for a reaction.

"I'm from Florida and used to see you at the club all the time. When I heard you were in town, I just had to see what it was that made you turn down everything you had. Now I know. I came forward and gave my life to God tonight."

"That's fantastic! That really makes me happy," Sammy smiled. "Let me sign this."

> "May this album help you to always remember the unfulfilling life you once lived, and help you to be thankful for the happiness you've now discovered."
> —Sammy Hall

"Take care, I'll be praying for you," Sammy said before disappearing behind the curtain.

While drinking a Coke, a well-dressed, clean-cut man came up to Sammy's side. "Mr. Hall," the man said, although Sammy was still sipping his Coke, his left eye peering from one side of the can at the stranger. "I'm Reverend Clarke, Pastor of the Lutheran Covenant Church."

"It's a pleasure to meet you," Sammy replied, setting his Coke down.

"You've got a real unusual style of ministry," the Reverend offered.

"To most standards, I guess you could say that."

"Well, we're very interested in discussing your methods with you."

"Who's 'we'?" Sammy asked.

"Oh, I'm sorry. I'm the chairman of our city's Council of Churches. We're having a luncheon tomorrow, and we'd be honored to have you as our guest."

Sammy felt out of place the moment he walked in. Everyone was dressed in their three-piece suits or clergy garbs. He was wearing his Sammy Hall T-shirt, a new pair of blue jeans, and his cowboy boots. Even the bus-boys were better dressed for the occasion than he. Sammy was seated next to the chairman who was sitting to the right of the small podium. When he sat down, it reminded him of those Sundays he visited his parents' church. No one greeted him, just stared. "You'd think I was on trial," Sammy thought to himself.

A gray-haired priestly dressed man opened the meeting with a seemingly-memorized prayer, using such big words that Sammy could have understood it just as well if it had been in Hebrew.

"What kind of steak is this?" Sammy asked the gentleman to his left.

The man responded with a quick, but harsh, "New York."

"Mine's real good, how's yours?" Sammy inquired.

"OK," he said, turning his head the opposite direction to avoid further conversation.

Then Reverend Clarke stood to the podium and formally introduced Sammy, receiving no applause, which immediately had him worried.

"Most of you have been to at least one of his meetings the last several nights. Whatever your feelings are toward his ministry, you must admit it's unique. Now Sammy, would you mind if we asked you a few questions?"

"No, I guess not," Sammy answered, although uncertain as to what they had in mind.

The first to stand was a middle-aged pastor whose dark hair and thick-rimmed glasses blended nicely with his dark suit. His white shirt was just a shade brighter than his pale skin and the touch of grey protruding from his scalp.

"I'm Reverend Silas Barnes. Tell me, Mr. Hall, do you feel the way you dance and sing rock-n-roll is pleasing to God?"

"First of all," Sammy said calmly, "you've got to realize everything I do up there is being done unto the Lord. If I'm moving to the beat, dancing as you call it, or if I'm singing loud music—as long as I'm doing it unto God, He can't help but be pleased."

"Those kids don't know the attitude or motivation behind your show," the pastor responded. "All they see is some long-haired, fancy-dressed rock singer."

"Hold on, Reverend. This is not a show. It's a crusade to tell people about Jesus Christ. And besides, how can you say they aren't getting my message? Did you see how many came forward last night?"

The man snapped back, "Well, the way I see it, your music got them so emotionally pumped up that they would have done anything you asked. Rock-n-roll music puts a kid right at your fingertips. It's of Satan," he added.

"That makes a lot of sense!" Sammy shook

his head. "Satan uses rock to bring kids down and accept Christ. That's ridiculous!"

"Does anyone else have a question or comment?" the chairman broke in awkwardly.

"I do," said a man, almost a replica of the previous minister except for being overweight. "How do we know you're a dedicated Christian?"

"I'll tell ya, it seems to me," Sammy said, "I wouldn't have given up all the money and fame I had in the music business to travel around in a bus telling others about God if I didn't believe in Him. And besides, what right do you have to question my relationship with God anyway? If you think this is of Satan then maybe you should question your own salvation," he said angrily.

Immediately, the noise level rose as emotionless faces turned to frowns.

"I'll be blunt," Reverend Clarke exclaimed. "I don't think these meetings should continue. If we, as the spiritual leaders of this community, don't stand up against it the people in our churches are going to think we're condoning it."

Heads started to nod in agreement as Sammy rose from his chair, pondering whether he should wave his white napkin to signal his surrender or whether to walk out.

"It seems as if none of you have listened to what I've said. But at least pay attention to what I have to say now. There are kids out there who your churches aren't reaching," pointing out the door. "Your churches are full of Sunday church-goers who care more about putting a dollar in an offering plate and driving to church in their cadillacs than they do about the runaways, drug addicts and thousands of young people being misled by the cults. And yet you waste your time condemning me for trying to share Christ with them!" Sammy said astonishedly. "I'm sorry. No one stops God's crusades except God Himself," tossing his napkin on his plate before walking out. "Oh, before I leave, you're all invited to tonight's meeting. The altar call should start about 10:00."

"Sammy!" a young man from a back table hollered before he was out the door. "Hold on. I just wanted you to know everyone here isn't against you. You've got my support. And I'd even wear a Sammy Hall T-shirt to prove it if I had one," he mused.

"Thanks, I appreciate that," Sammy said, grinning at the nicely-groomed preacher. "And I'll definitely get you a T-shirt. I'd give the rest of you one, but you'd probably baptize it in dishwater or burn it as a sacrifice."

Driving back to the hotel, Sammy beat his fist against the steering wheel. "Why does it have to be so hard? I'm doing my best to serve you, and you let this kind of garbage get in my way. I'm tired of it." Doubts began to taunt him. "Maybe I should go back to singing traditional music. At least no one hassles me. Maybe this whole thing is just me and God has nothing to do with it."

The light turned green, but although the hotel was straight ahead, Sammy made a right into a park. A boy was playing fetch with his dog when the ball just missed Sammy's head after ricocheting off a picnic table. In the distance a couple was sitting under a tree, and to the right was a little-league baseball game. Parents circled the backstop with their blankets, patio chairs and cushions, their thermoses growing out of the grass, watching their sons proudly.

"Most likely some of those kids are going to have drug problems and possibly commit crimes. If only they could stay young, shielded from reality," Sammy thought. Suddenly his hopes were broken by the cries of a girl in back of him. Evidently, she'd fallen off her swing, her mother rushing to the rescue. The other kids paid no atention, continuing to play on the slide, teeter-totter, and monkeybars.

"Father," Sammy whispered to himself as he made his way to a bench, "I need you to rush to my aid right now."

"Hey, mister, got a light?" a kid on his ten-speed bike asked.

"No, I don't."

"Mister, is something wrong?" he asked, noticing the tears flowing from beneath Sammy's sunglasses.

"No, I'm okay," Sammy paused. "What's your name?"

"Phil. What's yours?"

"Sammy Hall."

"You must be the guy who's been preaching and singing and stuff at my school this week."

"Yeah, that's right. Have you had a chance to come?"

"Nope. I get enough of that junk on Sundays. I've got better things to do with my time."

"Well, what are you doing tonight?"

"I've gotta . . . uh . . . I, um . . . I'm not sure. Oh, I know! I gotta take care of my little brother."

"Bring him along," Sammy suggested.

"Maybe. I gotta go," the boy rode off.

"Thanks Lord, I guess there really are kids that only my type of ministry can reach," Sammy said aloud.

An hour and a half before the service was to start, people were filing into the auditorium seeking a front row seat. As Sammy started across the unprepared stage, he was stunned by the crowd's enthusiastic reaction, and hurriedly shot behind the curtain, failing to set up the "mikes" as he'd intended.

"Why are all those people out there so early?" he asked his sister.

"They probably just found out their football games were cancelled," she answered.

"Cancelled? Since when?"

"I forgot to tell you. Some minister called and said he'd arranged to have this week's games postponed to encourage your meetings."

"A minister? What minister? Did he give you

his name?"

"No, but he said something about you owing him a T-shirt."

Smiling, Sammy returned to an office he was using as a prayer room. But his meditation was interrupted by several knocks.

"Mr. Hall?"

"Yes?"

"My name is Shelley Clarke. Could I talk with you a minute or so? It's real important," the tall, slender girl asked, her brown hair nearly covering one eye. The attractive young lady sat down as Sammy nodded his approval. "I saw you walk across the stage, and they told me I could find you back here. I hope you don't mind."

"No, no problem."

"I came to your meeting last night, and I, well, I need some help," she said shamefully, bowing her head.

"What kind of help, Shelley?" Sammy asked, glancing at the clock.

"You see, Mr. Hall, . . ."

"Call me Sammy," he broke in.

"Sammy," she affirmed, 'I'm . . . I'm . . . ," she muttered. "Oh, I don't know why I'm bothering you," she said bitterly, slamming the door behind her, running down the hallway.

Whipping the door open, leaning his head out, he yelled, "Shelley! Shelley!" but she'd disappeared.

The auditorium was full, aisles were nonexistent, entrances packed. Fathers lifted their children on their shoulders as mothers stood by wishing they had such a view. The burden of knowing that a girl in despair, needing a friend, was hopefully sitting out there, weighed heavily on Sammy as he ministered. Repeatedly, Sammy sang about giving all your problems to Christ; he quoted 1 Peter 5:7. *Casting all your cares on Him for He careth for you.* It was as though the message was just for Shelley, but others needed to hear it too.

Hundreds came forward to commit their lives to Christ. However, disappointedly, Sammy didn't see Shelley anywhere near the front. But walking toward the office, he noticed a light was on inside.

"Shelley! I'm glad you came back, but how'd you get in?"

"I'm a master of the ID card," she answered.

"Well?" tilting his head to one side.

"Well, what?" she replied.

"Well, do you want to talk about your problem?"

"Well, I guess that's why I'm here, but can I trust you?"

"Trust me with what?" he asked.

"If I tell you something, you promise not to tell anyone, not even my father?"

"I don't even know your father, do I?"

"Yeah, he's the Reverend Clarke."

"Oh," Sammy remarked, "I see. Why don't you talk to him about this?"

"If you were pregnant, would you tell your dad?" She began to cry, turning her back to him. "I'm not even sure who the father is."

Sammy got up from his chair and hugged her firmly to his chest, brushing his comforting hands over her hair. "It's going to be all right. God's going to work it all out." As her crying faded, taking a step back, Sammy asked, "Do you believe God can take care of everything?"

"I think He could if He wanted to," stopping to wipe the tears from her eyes, "but why would He help someone who's committed this kind of sin?"

"Don't feel guilty; all God expects is for you to feel sorry and ask His forgiveness. If you've done that, He doesn't hold it against you."

"Then how come my father wouldn't forgive me? I got caught using 'grass' a month ago, before I found out I was pregnant, and he told me I was a disgrace to the family and that unless I changed I wasn't his daughter anymore. I've even considered getting an abortion I'm so afraid of him, but I can't do it."

"I can't speak for your dad, but what counts right now is that you get yourself right with God," Sammy noted.

"I did that at last night's meeting. I was so happy; I wanted to tell my dad, but he was saying all this stuff about how all you cared about was entertaining and looking professional with your coordinated 'costumes' and fancy bus. I just couldn't tell him."

"I understand, but you know you've got to tell him everything sooner or later. Now that you've turned the whole thing over to God, things can't help but work out," Sammy said.

"I believe it." Shelley shook her head. "I've got to. He's my last hope."

While waiting to go on for the last night of the crusade, the unwed mother dashed up the back steps to the stage. "Sammy! Can I say a few words tonight?" she whispered anxiously.

"Do you really want to?"

"Uh huh."

"OK. It'll be in a little while, so have a seat," he said, making his way to the open stage.

"Sammy!" she said in a pleasant tone, "I asked my father to come tonight." Sammy responded by jerking his head back toward her even though he was visible to the people.

Shelley spoke boldly that night about God's love and mercy. "God's forgiven me," she said, "and He expects you to do the same." When she finished, people began to pray throughout the complex, and her face shone with the joy of a slave finding freedom. Yet there was no sign of her father.

Walking to the bus, having just dropped off their room keys at the hotel office, a red Volkswagen trailed by a police car pulled up beside Sammy.

"Sammy! We need to talk with you,"

Reverend Clarke said as he and his daughter hopped from the car, "but let me see what he wants first," motioning to the policeman. "I don't know what my daughter has done, but she's all straightened out now," the Reverend said sternly. "I'm her father, and I can promise she's not going to get in any more trouble. Please let her go."

"Mister," the policeman stated, "I don't know what you're talking about. You're the one in trouble. You just ran a red light."

Walking over to Sammy, one arm around his daughter, the Reverend offered his apology. "Seeing Shelley up there last night made me realize I was wrong. I don't know what more I can say but that I'm sorry and I hope you come back."

"Apology accepted," Sammy responded, shaking hands.

"Yeah Dad, we forgive you," Shelley smiled.

Chapter 6

The Great Loss

Water flowed across the newly-waxed linoleum onto the multi-colored carpet as Jacki came running, her arms full of towels. Realizing the towels weren't enough to soak up what was now becoming a pond, Jacki attempted to wrap cloths around the broken pipe, only to get a squirt in the face almost as powerful as that from a firehose, sending her sprawling backward into the water.

"Oh God, why does he always have to be gone?" she cried, up to her wrists in water, her pants drenched. "Whenever anything goes wrong Sammy's off somewhere. Don't either of you care about me?"

Finally getting the water turned off, Jackie waded through ankle-deep water to find a broom to sweep the water out the sliding door.

"Hey, Mom!" Monte yelled. "Wow, this place is a mess. Hey Mom, where are ya?"

"I'm in here," she hollered back.

"What happened?" he asked.

"Oh, the stupid pipe broke."

"Can I go over to Tim's for a little while?"

"No, not now," she said without looking at him.

"Why not, Mom? Everybody's gonna be there. C'mon!"

"I said 'no'!"

"But Mom," Monte begged.

"Here, take these," handing him some towels, "We're going to clean this place up."

"Let's call a plumber," Monte suggested. "Let him clean it up."

"Plumbers don't clean up your water, they just fix your pipes and clean out your pockets," she replied.

"I sure wish Dad was here," Monte said, ringing out the dripping towel in the sink.

"I do too," Jacki shook her head, although thinking to herself that someday God was going to reward their faithfulness and things would get better.

Meanwhile, Sammy's career was blossoming even further. He had made 14 gospel recordings and sung in all the major concerts around the country and Europe. Singing in front of crowds of 15,000 was more common than not. Thousands of young people were coming to know the Lord. But still the offerings weren't enough to always live comfortably. Jacki was still making all their clothes and giving haircuts, they had moved into a mobile home in Tennessee, and at times it was hard to make ends meet. But worst of all, Sammy was constantly on the road.

Jacki not only became the plumber when pipes broke, but she was also the gardener to growing weeds, the disciplinarian to disobedient children, the financial manager of a small bank account, and the childbearer of her seldom seen husband's children.

Monte—

I've gone to the doctor. Will be back shortly. Fix yourself a sandwich. There's peanut butter and jelly in the refrigerator.

Love, Mom

"Mrs. Hall, it's good to see you. How's the mommy doing?" the lady doctor asked.

"Just fine."

"Why don't you lay down on the table and we'll get right to checking you out," motioned the attractive doctor in her white lab coat. "Well, the baby is looking good," she smiled, feeling Jacki's stomach for its positioning.

"How much longer do you think I have to go?" Jacki asked.

"I'd say about five weeks."

"But that's way past nine months," Jacki exclaimed.

"Some women just have longer pregnancies than others. Don't worry, five more weeks after about eight months is nothing. Now lay real still so I can get the baby's heartbeat," she said, moving the stethoscope around to get the clearest sound.

"That thing is cold!" Jacki squirmed.

"Sorry," the doctor answered with a puzzled look on her face. "Do you have a history of twins in your family?"

"No, not that I know of. Why?"

"I thought I was picking up two heartbeats. How 'bout your husband's family; have they had twins?"

"I don't think so."

"It was probably just the baby tapping up against your stomach. Besides, if it was twins we would have most likely known a while back. It's nothing to worry about."

"Good," Jacki responded peculiarly.

In the waning weeks Jacki never considered the joy of having twins, for the fear of complications overwhelmed her thoughts. At times she lay still, hoping to feel just one heartbeat, any heartbeat. Five weeks passed and the doctor kept delaying the arrival date. "It may be as much as three more weeks," she had said.

"Sammy, wake up! I think it's time."

"Go back to sleep, it's not time to get up yet," Sammy said drowsily.

"I mean it's time. The baby's coming. We've got to get to the hospital."

"Why didn't you say so?" frantically

throwing the covers off the bed, hopping to his feet. "Are you OK?"

"Yes, can you help me put on my robe?"

"Where is it?" Sammy asked, rummaging through the closet.

"It's on the door knob."

"Here, slip on your slippers, too," Sammy said, setting them in front of her feet, then throwing on his jeans, a sport coat over his pajama top, and his white tennis shoes. "Let's go," motioning her to the door.

"You've got to call the hospital," she reminded him.

"That's right," Sammy nodded, running back into the house and out again in less than a minute. "How ya feelin'?" he asked, going 50 in a 30 mph zone.

"I'll be just fine; just hurry up and get there," she said, her eyes closed.

"We're a block away; hold on."

They were greeted by a nurse with a wheelchair parked in front of her. "Have a seat and we'll take care of you," she said comfortingly, patting Jacki on the shoulder. "You'll be fine. Sir, you can wait in the waiting room; the nurse at the front desk will tell you where it is."

Sammy watched Jacki all the way down the hall before advancing to the receptionist's desk.

"Ma'am, my wife's having a baby and the . . ."

"I can tell," she interrupted.

"How's that?"

"Only expecting fathers come in dressed like that," pointing to his comical appearance.

"You're probably right," running his fingers through his hair. "Anyway, could you show me how to get to the waiting room?"

"Up the elevator one floor and two hallways to the left. You can't miss it. And don't worry, most husbands come in looking worse than what you've got on."

But inside the waiting room there sat a middle-aged man in a tan three-piece suit, every hair greased in place, smoking a cigar.

"Hi pops," the man waved.

"Hi," Sammy glanced back strangely.

"Is this your first?" the man asked.

"No, my second," Sammy replied. "Your first?"

"Huh," he laughed. "This is my fifth. So far all girls, but I'm hoping for a boy this time."

"You mean your wife hasn't already delivered?"

"Not yet, but I should hear any time now."

"Aren't you supposed to wait on the cigars until after your baby arrives?"

"That's just tradition. I've found it relaxes me until I get the word. Here, have one," he offered.

"No thanks, I don't smoke."

"I've heard that so many times over the years; I've come prepared. How 'bout a lollipop?" the man asked, pulling a handful from his pocket.

"Sure," Sammy responded, trying to avoid

offending the man.

"Mr. Ward," the nurse entered, "it's another girl and your wife's fine. You can see them both in about 15 minutes."

"Thanks nurse," he said, although Sammy could see his disappointment as the once talkative man sat quietly.

"It's been about 15 minutes," the man said, looking at his watch. "I guess I'd better get in there. Good luck."

"You too, and thanks for the sucker," Sammy smiled.

An hour passed and still no word from the doctor. Whenever someone passed, the doors would rattle and Sammy would jerk his head up from its prone position, only to catch a glimpse of a figure passing by the small window. As more people walked by without entering the room Sammy's concern grew. Finally, he went back to the front desk.

"Could you check on my wife? She's been in there over two hours," Sammy asked.

"Sir, there's nothing to be alarmed about. Sometimes it takes over 10 hours. But if you don't hear in another hour, I'll see what I can find out. All you can do is wait. I'm sure it will soon be over."

Meanwhile, the delivery room had a cold, dungeon-like atmosphere. Sweat poured off the doctors' and nurses' brows, soaking through their hair covers and masks. The air was heavy, the light seemed dimmed. The life of one baby had turned this room of usual beauty into a morgue of ugliness. Only moments before, the thrill of expentancy radiated from their faces.

"I think this is going to be a big one," one nurse commented.

"It should be,' the doctor replied, "she's 10 months pregnant."

"Doctor! Doctor, I can't get the baby's heartbeat," an aide shouted.

"What d'ya mean?" she said, desperately grabbing the stethoscope. "Nurse, go tell Mr. Hall complications have arisen. Don't tell him what. Just say we're doing all we can, but it may be a while."

The nurse reluctantly turned toward the door, slowly, wishing she wasn't the messenger. Carefully she walked down the hallway, trying to gather her thoughts, stopping outside the waiting room for a deep breath. Agonizingly she pushed the door open to find Sammy in deep thought, leaning over, his elbows on his knees, staring at the magazines on the table.

"Mr. Hall."

"Uh-huh."

"The doctor sent me to tell you that some complications have arisen and it may be awhile."

"What kind of complications?"

"I'm not sure, Mr. Hall."

"Well, she's going to be OK, isn't she?"

"I don't know the extent of the problem. I'm sorry, I just don't know."

"Can't I talk to someone who does?" Sammy asked emphatically.

"Everyone is in the delivery room. I wish I could tell you more, but I can't. But we'll let you know as soon as we find something."

Back in the delivery room the doctors had given up hope of saving the baby and were concentrating on saving Jacki. When she woke up, she knew something was wrong. "Did my baby die?" she mumbled.

"Yes, I'm afraid it did. I'm sorry, but we did all we could," the doctor answered.

"What happened?" Jackie cried, covering her eyes with her hand.

"Evidently the baby has been dead for some time now. You're such a healthy young lady your body didn't reject it as it normally would."

"Why did it die?" Jacki questioned, her face pressing against the sheets.

"Remember when I said I thought I heard two heartbeats? Well, I have reason to believe your baby actually had two hearts. Maybe it was trying to split into twins and for some reason the process wasn't completed. We don't know yet."

"Where's my husband?"

"He's in the waiting room. I was just going to tell him."

"No, please, let me tell him."

"Fine, I'll send him in," she said.

The smile he expected to see on Jacki's face wasn't there. It was somewhere underneath her clenched face.

"Honey," rushing to her side, grabbing her hand. "Why are you crying?" he asked, looking around. "Are you OK? Where's the baby?"

"Sammy, I lost it," Jacki wept.

Sammy's eyelids slowly closed, trying to soothe the sudden jolt of pain.

"The doctor said it had two . . . ," she said, unable to finish.

"Two what?" he asked, putting his hand on the damp washcloth on her forehead. "It's OK, two what?"

"Hearts."

"Well, Jacki, you know as well as I do that God's got everything under control. The child might have suffered tremendously if it lived."

"I know, but that was our baby," she began to cry again.

"It's all right," clutching her head, "we'll have some more."

"Mr. Hall, excuse me, but could I talk with you a second outside?" the doctor asked, poking her head in the door. "Has your wife told you what we think happened to your baby?"

"Yes, she said it had two hearts," Sammy choked, fighting back tears of his own.

"That's right. I don't want to force you to do anything, and I know this probably isn't the right time to ask you this, but we need to know right away. Would you consider donating your child to the University of Tennessee for study purposes?"

Sammy stared at her as if to say "You're crazy." "I'm sorry, doctor, but Jacki would never go for that."

"Your baby may prevent this from happening to some parents down the line. At least think about it."

"OK, I will, but I've got a question for you. When I was growing up, I had some involvement with drugs. Could that be the cause of this?"

"I can't be sure but it's highly unlikely," she said.

As Sammy re-entered the room, Jacki had settled down a little. "Listen Jacki, they want us to donate our baby to science so they can prevent this type of thing from happening."

"No way, they're not dissecting my baby!"

"But Jacki, do you want others to go through this?"

"Of course not, I just don't want to remember my baby as a classroom conversation piece."

"Look at it this way then. The first baby they save from this deformity will be a child our child helped save."

"It's up to you," she nodded.

Two days later, Sammy's first step onto the bus was a hard one to take. Leaving Jacki to go through the misery and discouragement alone was difficult. Bernice, Sammy's sister, stayed with her for a short while, but Sammy didn't want to go on tour until things were back to normal. Hour upon hour Sammy's eyes stared at the rolling hills, stars and highways from the moving bus, yet rarely did they register what they had seen. Sammy's inner eyes were hundreds of miles back imagining what Jacki was experiencing. Meanwhile, Jacki felt like an abandoned orphan, comfortlessly carrying the burden alone.

Chapter 7

Kidnapped

Laying on her stomach in bed, one arm slung over the side, the other tucked neatly under the pillow, Jacki woke suddenly to the irritating, but effective "beeps" of her digital alarm clock. Crawling from the comfort of the warm covers and soothing mattress wasn't easy, but she'd decided the night before to give the trailer a thorough cleaning. It took her little time to wrap her hair in a bun and get into her usual working clothes: faded jeans and one of Sammy's old shirts. The windows were washed, the colonial furniture dusted, the floors waxed, but the carpet needed more than vacuuming. So after dropping off Cori, her infant daughter, at the babysitter's, Jacki drove into town to rent a shampooer.

Upon entering the unpaved parking lot, dust rose everywhere into the humid air, surfacing on the hoods of the other three cars parked in a row beside Jacki's gold Monte Carlo. Stepping from the car her eyes were drawn to a poster on the window of the ice cream parlor across the street: a milk shake with cold drops of water running down the sides of the paper cup, and a straw invitingly protruding from the chocolate glaze. But any thoughts of indulging ceased abruptly when she caught a glance of a man staring at her from beside the poster, leaning against the wall, his hands buried in his pockets.

Even though the store didn't have the equipment to rent, Jacki came out carrying a sack full of items. The previously hidden sun had peeked out from behind the clouds, and the heat from the steaming pebbles seemed to penetrate her soles like they were made of paper.

Scurrying to the car, she flung the sack in the back seat and hurriedly scooted inside in hopes that the air conditioner would cool her sun-battered body. Attempting to close the door Jacki was greeted with a violent, unshaven face glaring at her from his squatted position between the car and the opened door.

"How do ya get ta Greenville?" he asked harshly, ducking to keep out of sight. "How do I get to Greenville?" he repeated, cussing at her.

Too startled to answer right back, Jacki said nervously, "I don't know."

"Where is it?" he snarled.

"You, you . . . I think you . . . I'm not sure; I'm sorry," she stuttered, trying to close the door.

"You'd better remember in a hurry lady, or you're a dead lady," pulling a gun wedged inside his pants, hidden by his shirt. The barrel was so long and intimidating that at first Jacki thought it was just a toy.

"I remember now," Jacki said.

"I thought you would."

"I'm pretty sure you go about five miles past the stop light, make a right onto the highway; no, I think it's a left."

"Make sure, lady."

"It's definitely a left, and follow the signs," she said, although truthfully unsure where the town was.

"Just to make sure you're not sending me on a wild goose chase," he snarled, "you're coming with me. Move over! Don't mess with me lady. I said move over," putting the gun to her head.

"I've got three children," Jacki cried. "Please let me go. Don't hurt me. You can have the car, just let me go."

"I don't care about your kids. All I care about is getting to Greenville. Now, if you shut up and quit the cryin' I'll let you off outa town. Now shut up!" he yelled.

Any thoughts Jacki entertained about making a run for it were squelched by the sight of his gun and the locked door on her side.

Just then a large customer came from the store. Jackie tried to signal him by making her terrified face and streaming tears visible. She even slyly tried to alert him with her hands, but to no avail. The man paid no attention.

Jerking her arm down and shoving the gun

into her side, he angrily whispered, "If you try anything, I'll kill you. Just cut the noise and sit still."

"It doesn't bother you that I'm a mother of three babies, and I've got a husband? Please let me go."

"Will you shut up?" he screamed. "Do you wanna die? How do ya get this seat back?" he slurred, laying the gun on the console to put more pressure on the seat. "Oh, forget it," he said, pulling out of the parking lot.

His stringy blonde hair hung wildly over the collar of his roughed-up leather jacket. The right pocket had been torn and fastened back together with a large safety pin. But Jacki could see that although the stocky, 5'7" fellow talked tough and looked mean, he was as scared as she was.

Jacki continued to cry and pray to herself. "Oh, God, please Lord, help me; save me Jesus. I need you," she repeated, knowing that after the stoplight it was a long four-lane highway, on which anything could happen. She realized the danger of the seldom used highway in the middle of nowhere, imagining him pulling off to the side of the road, and dragging her back into the woods to shoot her, or getting shot and thrown over a cliff. These horrifying thoughts assured her something had to be done before they reached that light.

"Lord, help me," she prayed. For the first time in her life Jacki heard God speak to her heart, as God had spoken to Sammy times before. "Jacki, get out of the car," He said.

"But God, we're going at least 45 mph."

"Just get out of the car."

As they came up to a road construction area, they slowed down to about 35 mph. Cleverly, Jacki snuck her left hand through the straps of her purse she wore over her right shoulder, and in a sudden motion flipped the lock open and plunged into the working area. She rolled and bounced onto the pavement into a trench of loose gravel, painting bruises all over her skin, carving scrapes into her elbows and knees, and nearly missing a construction worker holding a 'SLOW' sign. There she lay, conscious, agonizing in pain, blood trickling into the rocks, yet perfectly still.

The workers were so bewildered they stood still for a second themselves, finding it hard to believe what they'd seen. The kidnapper was stunned himself and floored the Monte Carlo through a red light, sideswiping two cars.

Finally, one man came to her aid. "Are you all right?"

"I don't think anything's broken," as she tried to get up.

"Stay down," the man nudged her shoulder. "Relax. Hey, Paul!" he yelled, "Take the truck and go call an ambulance. And hurry."

Shortly, a large group of perspiring, bare-chested men, their tools still in their hands, had gathered around her. "C'mon, hop in," a man yelled from a stopped car. Without hesitation she found herself, bleeding sores and all, climbing into a car with a stranger for the second time in one day. But this man was the tall gentleman she had tried to signal at the store.

"Was that your husband?"

"No, he kidnapped me," she began to cry, rubbing her arms to calm the pain.

"Well, I was going to say if he was your husband, it might be wise to find a new one. I've been following you from the store, but I didn't want to let on I knew something was wrong, because he probably would have done you more harm."

"Thanks so much," Jacki praised.

"We'll get to the police station first so they can get right on this guy's trail, and then I'll take you to the hospital if you need to go. But just relax, it's all over," he comforted. "Everything's going to be all right."

But things momentarily got worse as Jacki was nearly hysterical when the police officer dabbed alcohol on her raw flesh wounds. Puss flowed and blood continued to drip as she nearly passed out.

"Oh, that hurts!" she screamed. "What are you trying to do, kill me? Stop it!"

"I know it hurts, but it's got to be done," he said.

"I don't care. If I didn't know any better I'd think you were related to the kidnapper," she frowned.

While making out the police report, Jacki received word the car had been found abandoned on a side road off the highway. But in chasing the fugitive on foot he escaped into a jungle of bushes and trees.

Jacki couldn't believe this entire plot was real. It was one of those things she'd seen in the movies, but never imagined happening to her. She was the star of her own nightmare.

That night television and radio reports of the episode flooded the airwaves.

"Jacki Hall, wife of gospel rock idol Sammy Hall, was abducted today and escaped at gun point by diving from a moving vehicle." Reports kept coming in. But reporters weren't satisfied with the information they had, and flocked to the trailer for a mini-news conference.

"Mrs. Hall?" one reporter asked. "Do you believe the kidnapper had a ransom plan in mind?"

"I don't think so, he was just trying to reach Greenville."

"Why Greenville?"

"I don't know," she answered.

"Has your husband been notified?" an older, wrinkle-faced man inquired.

"No, not yet; I've been unable to reach him. He's at a crusade in Missouri."

"Have you ever seen this man before?"

"Nope."

"Do you think he'll come back after you, especially since you misled him?" the first reporter questioned.

The thought hadn't crossed Jacki's mind until now. "Would he come back?" she wondered, trembling at the thought of seeing that terrifying face eye to eye again. "I'm sorry, but that's all the questions I can answer right now. Please excuse me," she said, stepping back into the trailer.

Fifteen minutes later an unexpected knock sent Jacki flying from her chair in panic. Peeking from the window she was relieved to see police officers. "Sorry to bother you this late, Mrs. Hall, but we wanted to see if you could spot the guy in these books of mugshots."

She examined page after page, face after face without finding anyone resembling her abductor. Suddenly she winced backward at the sight of the stringy-haired man gleaming at her from the middle of the page.

"That's him! I know it's him," Jacki began crying, chills running up her back.

"Are you sure?"

Unable to stop the tears long enough to speak, she shook her head and shoved the book away.

"Put out an alert along with a description for escaped convict, Matthew Sims," one officer told the other. "We've been on the look-out for him about a week now. We know he's robbed several houses up north. I think that's probably where he got the gun."

"Do you think he'll come back here?" Jackie sniffled.

"Nah, don't worry about that. He'd be a fool to come back here. He knows we're looking for him in these parts. He won't be back," he promised.

Even his reassurances didn't relieve her fears. After he left, her anxiety mounted, feeling alone, helpless and prey to a free roaming maniac. Jacki had called Sammy numerous times, and when she finally reached him she wasn't the calm, together person she'd planned on being.

"Sammy?"

"Yeah Hon, how's it goin'?"

"Not too well; I got kidnapped today.,"

"That's funny, so did I," he teased, thinking it was a joke.

"Sammy, I'm serious. He put a gun to my head and threatened to kill me and everything," she whined.

"Slow down, Jacki. You mean you really got kidnapped?"

"Uh-huh!"

"Well, what happened? Tell me about it," he said calmly.

After she'd told him the story, Sammy tried to comfort her without getting upset, because he knew that would only compound the problem. "Take it easy Jacki; I'll be home in a couple of days."

"But I need you now. I don't want to stay here by myself," she begged, trying to get his sympathy.

"I can't come home now. You'll be OK. Don't

worry; I'll be back as soon as I can."

"Don't you care about me, Sammy? Cuz if you do, you'll come back right now."

"I can't come right now. If you want, get one of your friends to stay with you."

"Just forget it. Sing your songs and make a lot of people happy, but just remember what your wife is going through," she said angrily, considering hanging up.

"Jacki! Now listen to me a second. We're going to pray over the phone, because you know as well as I do that God can protect you and comfort you better than I can anyway.

"Dear God, we don't understand why you allow things like this to take place, but we do know you've got everything under control. We pray, Lord, that you'll comfort Jacki tonight, and give her a peace that will relieve all her fears.

"Do you feel any better?"

"Yeah, but I still really need you."

"I know you do, but I just can't leave. You know that."

"I'm afraid, Sammy."

"We just prayed, and if you'll trust in God, you'll have a good night's sleep. I love you, Jacki."

"I love you too," she responded. "See you soon."

It was a night of horror. The shrieking door, the noisy crickets, and passing automobiles all brought terror into Jacki's bedroom. It was impossible to sleep, and television was no longer on the air; the radio was the last resort. But a news report that an escaped convict was still on the loose drove Jacki to turn off the radio, burying herself under the covers.

That face kept reappearing in front of her on the curtains, ceiling, lampshades and everywhere, even in her thoughts. It was deeply imprinted in her mind. "God!" she yelled. "Help me! Take him away. Let me sleep."

Then it dawned on her how much God had helped her through the ordeal already. If she'd taken Cori with her to town, Jacki wouldn't have been able to jump from the car. And how that road construction area enabled her to jump out at a slower speed, protecting her from serious injury.

But again the feeling of that gun pressing up against her head, and the thought of her life weighing on one pull of a trigger rekindled her fears. She couldn't sleep, imagining her captor climbing through her window, a knife clenched between his teeth in pirate-like fashion, ready to finish her off. Jacki flew out of bed, checking the windows and doors, and grabbing a steak knife to put next to the bed just in case.

Needless to say, Sammy's return was a big relief to Jacki. But the fear of staying at home while Sammy was on the road was still there, persuading her to do more traveling with Sammy in the coming years. A few weeks later they received word the criminal had been apprehended in Florida, further easing Jacki's worries.

"That was the police station on the phone," Sammy yelled to Jacki in the bedroom. "They want us to come down and formally press charges."

"I won't have to see him again, will I?" she asked.

"You probably will if it goes to court."

"Then I don't want to press charges."

"But Jacki, this guy should be punished for what he's done."

"I don't care; I've suffered enough without having to relive seeing him again," she embraced Sammy, her head resting on his shoulder. "Let's just let it end; please let it end."

Sammy patted her on the back. "OK, it's over," he said as he kissed the top of her head.

Years later it was learned the kidnapper admitted to killing 12 women. Truly Jacki had been delivered from danger.

Chapter 8

A New Direction

A large gold-framed mirror reflected Sammy throwing his luggage on the floor and dropping wearily on the bed. The room was plushly decorated, a chandelier hanging helplessly above a small colonial table and a floor-length curtain hiding a sliding glass door which led to a balcony with a view of vibrant Detroit. But the bed was the only thing Sammy saw.

Closing his eyes, he thought about the exhausting tour and his need for a change. He had accomplished just about everything in the gospel music business, and desired a new direction, a new mountain to climb, a new challenge which would still allow him to lead people to God.

"Hello?" Sammy answered the phone.

"Hello; could I speak to Sammy Hall please?"

"Speaking."

"Hi, my name is Don Held; I'm a friend of Alice and Grover Canon."

"Oh yes," Sammy responded.

"They played one of your albums for me recently. I'll tell you Sammy, your music really touched me. You've got a special talent."

"Thank you, I appreciate that," Sammy paused. "What was your name again?"

"Don Held."

"Well, thanks for the call, Mr. Held," trying to end the conversation and get some rest.

"I need to ask you something before you go. That's the main reason I called," the man said. "Would you be available to sing tomorrow morning at a convention?"

"Where's this convention at?"

"Charlotte, North Carolina."

"What?" Sammy laughed. "What time tomorrow?"

"In time for the 11:00 service," he answered.

"I'd be pretty rushed to make it, I don't know. What denomination are you associated with?" Sammy asked.

"Oh, it's not a denominational thing. Have you ever heard of Amway?"

"Sure," Sammy replied.

"Well, this is a Dexter Yager—Amway Free Enterprise convention, and we have a regular church service on Sunday morning. We'd be thrilled to have you come," he said.

"I'll tell you the truth, Mr. Held. I haven't had any sleep for almost two days now, and if I flew to North Carolina tomorrow morning there are so many things I'd have to do before I left that I wouldn't get any sleep tonight either. I just think it's too late."

"I know it's a last minute thing, but I've been trying to reach you for two days. You're a hard man to get a hold of," Mr. Held said disappointedly.

"I doubt I could even get a flight," Sammy said.

"If you don't come you're missing out on an opportunity of a lifetime. I even contacted your friend Paul Conn about you. He'd be the first to tell you it's a great opportunity. I promise, you won't be sorry if you come."

"Let me see if I can get a flight," Sammy agreed, "and if you'll give me your number I'll call you right back."

Sammy found himself on the "red-eye" flight, a blanket mummied around him, trying to catch some sleep. His eyes wore circles, his speech was slow, and his temperament grumpy.

"Sir," the stewardess shouted into his ear.

"What's wrong?" Sammy awakened startled, fearing the plane might have engine trouble.

"Nothing's wrong, I just thought you might like something to drink."

"You woke me up just for a drink?"

"I'm sorry, sir; I won't disturb you again."

"That's OK, I'm just exhausted, that's all."

When Sammy left the plane he was met by a black-suited man twirling a black cap in his hands.

"Mr. Hall?"

"Yes, that's right."

"I'm your chauffeur."

The ever-so-long shining black limousine, with its caressing seats and deep shag carpet, almost put Sammy to sleep. He would have given anything to stretch out on the back seat for several hours. But as they arrived in front of the monstrous coliseum complex, nervousness replaced weariness.

Sitting backstage, Sammy heard thunderous roars rise and fall as often as a tide crashing against coastal rocks. He didn't know what to expect. How would they acknowledge him? How would they react to his music?

"Sammy, you made it," a man shook his hand. "I'm Don Held."

"Nice to meet you," Sammy smiled.

"How was your flight?"

"Just fine. You know, this is really incredible," Sammy motioned toward the audience.

"It really is," Don replied. "But you must be worn out."

"Right now I'm a little too nervous to be worried about sleep."

"Just do your thing, Sammy. I guarantee they'll love it," he grinned. "Listen, you go on in about 15 minutes, so just relax until I introduce you."

In no time Don had the "mike" in his hand—"It's a real privilege to introduce to you a man whose songs and testimony have brought many people to a relationship with Jesus Christ.

When I first heard his music I knew I wanted him to share at this convention," Don said, raising his hands to quiet the anxious crowd. "This is his first Amway performance, so let's give him the best applause he's ever had—welcome Sammy Hall!"

As Sammy made his way to the stage, clapping intensified, screaming crescendoed, and people eventually rose from their chairs. The standing ovation lasted several minutes as Sammy stood in awe. "This is incredible," he thought.

"Thank you very much, thank you," he said, calming them down slowly. "This is the most amazing crowd I've ever sung for," he added, once again bringing people from their chairs with voicetrous applause.

"I'm not going to say anything else because I want to get a chance to sing. But I do appreciate it." People sat on the edge of their seats the entire service, smiling, praying, and very attentive to his musical message.

When he'd finished, again they rose to their feet chanting "More, more, more." Sammy awarded them with another number as the plea for "more" continued. Before it was over he'd gone back for three or four bows. It was hard for Sammy to comprehend what had just occurred. He sat backstage drinking a cup of ice water, feeling drained, yet totally amazed at these people.

"Excuse me, excuse me, please let me

through," a lady said, rushing in Sammy's direction. "You were wonderful," she exclaimed, hugging him around the neck.

"Thank you very much," Sammy said.

"I was standing in the back, and I got 'goose bumps' just listening to you. I could tell you really believe what you were singing."

"Thanks, that means a lot," he nodded.

"I'm Birdie Yager; my husband is Dexter Yager."

"It's a pleasure to meet you. Thank you for inviting me," Sammy said.

"It's been our pleasure. I'd like you to meet all my kids."

"Sure," he agreed, following her through the lobby.

"Hey, Sammy Hall!" one kid yelled, and before he knew it he was swarmed by a large mob of autograph-seekers.

"Hold on, don't shove; everyone'll get their turn," Sammy declared, giving Birdie a look of helplessness.

"Sammy," Birdie called, "I'll go get them; go ahead and sign the autographs."

Having signed his name on everything from a cancelled check to a t-shirt, Birdie introduced her husband and children.

"Sammy, thanks for coming," Dexter said. "You were a big hit."

"Thanks for the invitation. This whole thing," Sammy spread his hands, "is just fantastic. These people are the greatest."

"I've been saying that for years," Dexter noted.

"All these people are in Amway?" Sammy asked.

"Yep. Had you ever heard of it?"

"Yeah, sure have, but I don't know exactly what it is."

"Well, maybe sometime I can show you what Amway's about."

"That would be great," Sammy replied.

"By the way, what would it take to get you to sing at my church tonight?" Dexter asked.

"Not much; I'd be happy to."

Leaving the coliseum in Dexter's coach, the crowd swarmed around the bus in almost riot-like fashion, but it was their love for Dexter Yager that moved them closer, hoping to see their hero and touch his coach. It amazed Sammy how one could be so well loved by so many people.

"Don't Let Anybody Steal Your Dream," Dexter yelled out his window, sending the crowd into hysteria, shouting "Dexter!" in unison as though he was a presidential candidate. It inspired Sammy as well, planting a dream in his own heart.

For the next four months Sammy had a longing to be part of what he'd experienced that unbelievable day in North Carolina. Finally, Dexter called and without pressure asked Sammy if he wanted to hear more about Amway. Sammy nearly jumped through the phone. "I sure would," he said.

Dexter and all his kids came to Sammy's home to explain the plan in person. Sammy respected Dexter for his willingness to share and give, but Jacki didn't know him and wasn't thrilled about a stranger and his "little league team" invading their house.

"Why's he coming anyway?" Jacki scorned. "Who does he think he is, inviting himself to our house? We hardly know the guy."

"I invited him. He's really a pleasant man; so be quiet and treat him nice. He should be here anytime," Sammy scolded.

Sure enough, the coach pulled up outside, and a group of smiling youngsters paraded out.

"Honey, this is Dexter Yager," Sammy introduced, "the one I've been telling you so much about. Dexter, this is my wife, Jacki."

"It's real nice to meet you, Jacki," Dexter said kindly.

"Hi," Jacki replied without cracking a smile.

After all the trivialities were out of the way and the two men were ready to talk business, Jacki entered following a long absence.

"I'm going to town," she sneered, grabbing her purse and heading for the door.

"Jacki," Dexter asked, "could I trouble you for a piece of paper?"

Without even looking she replied, "We don't have any paper. Oh, yes we do," tearing off a paper towel.

Dexter didn't bat an eye, although he knew

Jacki was upset. "Thanks, that'll do fine," he said, impressing Sammy even more. His humility and sincerity made Sammy figure that if this type of man is in this business then it must be a quality organization, and he signed up enthusiastically.

Jacki wasn't at all pleased. She wanted nothing to do with it. That is, until she attended a rally.

"Sammy! I don't want to go," she pleaded.

"Just go this one time," he said. "You won't have to go again if you don't want to."

"I know I won't like it. Just let me stay home."

"Please go. Just for me," he begged.

"All right, but just for you," she finally agreed.

When they arrived the friendly greeting they received made Jacki wonder if she had been a little hasty. But throughout the evening she sat statue-like, her eyes fixed straight ahead. She could feel herself becoming enthralled by the excitement and beauty of it all; but she could hear Sammy whispering in the back of her mind, "I told you so."

Occasionally, he would glance over at her to read her expressions. However, she concealed them well, trying to figure out a way of conceding Sammy was right, but saving face at the same time.

Riding home in the car, Sammy broke the silence.

"Well, what'd ya think?"
"Oh, it was," she paused, "nice."
"Was it what you expected," he asked.
"Yeah, pretty much."
"Did you like it?"
"It was OK," she replied.
"Just OK, huh?" Sammy said.
"No, it was nice. OK, I admit it, it was really nice. The people were wonderful and it looks like they've got a great thing goin'. But I'm going to have to go to a few more before I know if it's for me."
"Sounds good," Sammy shook his head, knowing it was only time before she gave her approval.
He was right. It wasn't long before Jacki had made a commitment to Amway, traveling from rally to crusade with Sammy and working hard to build the business.

Before leaving for a distant concert, Jacki sat in their coach waiting for Sammy, gazing at all the Lord had provided. "God surely rewards faithfulness," she thought, glancing at their 7,000 sq. ft. home with an indoor pool shaped like a guitar, and thinking about their numerous cars, coaches, mobile homes, employees and acres of land.
"Our ministry has also been blessed," Jacki said to herself, amazed by the 1,500,000 miles Sammy has traveled, and the 500,000 people won to Christ over his career.

As Sammy entered the coach Jacki met him with a question. "How far do we travel each year?"

"About 125,000 miles."

"And how many are saved each year, do you think?"

"Oh, probably 50,000. Why d'ya ask?"

"I don't know, I guess sometimes it's hard to believe how good God has been to us."

The engine's purr drowned out Sammy's response as they started the first mile of another journey to tell others about Jesus Christ.

The concert ballroom was packed, bulging out the doorways. The slide show had already started, and the band was getting the people warmed up for Sammy's entrance. Before their idol had even made it to the stage, kids and parents alike rushed to the front.

Suddenly, they all jumped back, as Sammy appeared through a cloud of smoke from a gimmick explosion, wearing a black and white leather outfit that was shockingly colorful. The place went wild. Multi-colored strobe lights were flashing as the mirror ball rotated. The crowd was waving banners; some were just singing and clapping along, children were jumping for joy while adults sat shedding tears. Meanwhile, Jacki sat backstage listening as if she was an avid fan, although she'd undoubtedly heard the songs many times before.

As Sammy began singing "*She Believes In*

Me", a slide of Jacki was flashed upon the screen, and she sauntered across the stage, her long black dress sparkling as were her eyes. Taking her hand, Sammy sang it to her, concluding with a kiss.

Sammy's tribute to Elvis Presley had people nearly crawling on the stage. Various scenes in the former rock hero's life were shown in the background as Sammy sang Elvis' biggest hits, moving hips and all. Scarfs worn around Sammy's neck were thrown to the audience as mobs of kids converged on them in piles.

The concert concluded with everyone holding hands singing "*Everybody Has a Dream.*" As he left the stage the crowd broke into a floor-shaking applause. Again and again Sammy took bows as the appreciation continued.

Finally, on his last return to the stage, a blonde-haired, blue-eyed little girl looked up at Sammy and said, "Sammy, promise me you'll never grow old."

Handing her a scarf and dotting her on the nose, Sammy kissed her on the forehead, saying, "I promise."

Once the concert was over, the crowd having departed to nearby restaurants and hotel rooms, the convention hall was transformed into a place of invisible meaning. The room was no longer filled with joyous applause, and the stage no longer radiated Sammy's music. Bus-boys hurriedly cleared the tables, janitors swept the floors, as Sammy's crew packed up his equipment. The excitement once generated in this room was gone, but not forgotten. The memory of Sammy Hall "becoming one" with his audience, singing from deep within, lives on.

To Reorder Books
Call or Write:

SAMMY HALL
P. O. Box 307
Sevierville, TN 37862

(615) 453-3905

$5.95